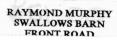

The
Chemical Engineering
Guide to Heat Transfer
Volume II
Equipment

Edited by

Kenneth J. McNaughton
and the Staff of Chemical Engineering

HEMISPHERE PUBLISHING CORPORATION
hpc Washington   New York   London

McGraw-Hill Publications Co., New York, N.Y.

DISTRIBUTION OUTSIDE NORTH AMERICA
SPRINGER-VERLAG

Berlin   Heidelberg   New York   Tokyo

Library of Congress Cataloging-in-Publication Data
Main entry under title:

The Chemical engineering guide to heat transfer.

  Includes bibliographies and index.
  Contents: v. 1. Plant principles—v. 2. Equipment.
  1. Heat—Transmission.   2. Heat exchangers.
I. McNaughton, Kenneth J.   II. Chemical engineering.
TJ260.C426   1985   660.2'8427   85-26987
ISBN 0-07-606939-7 (v. 1) Chemical Engineering
ISBN 0-07-606940-0 (v. 2) Chemical Engineering
ISBN 0-08116-465-0 (v. 1). Hemisphere
ISBN 0-89116-466-9 (v. 2) Hemisphere
DISTRIBUTED OUTSIDE NORTH AMERICA:
ISBN 3-540-16177-5 (v. 1) Springer-Verlag Berlin
ISBN 3-540-16178-3 (v. 2) Springer-Verlag Berlin

CONTENTS

PREFACE

When I was studying chemical engineering at college, I loved heat transfer. It was neat. Q = CAT. That's all I needed to know. And heat-in equals heat-out. Boy! If only the rest of life was so simple!

Some people say that engineers are drawn to science because they lack the skills to deal with people—that scientific types take comfort in being able to handle a field that responds according to inviolate laws, unlike their lawless and unpredictable fellow beings. Other observers, perhaps more charitable, suggest that those who inherit the skills to deal with a scientific universe may not give themselves the time to come to grips with the more elusive rules that attempt to explain human behavior.

I think both are fascinating fields worth pursuing. And who can say that the two won't come together? What with all the exciting developments in our understanding of molecular biology, surely we are overdue for some breakthroughs in psychology as well.

As it turns out, heat transfer isn't so simple anyway. But it is neat. And we are very fortunate to have developed our communication skills so well. In this book, for instance, we have accumulated ten years of practical wisdom from the pages of *Chemical Engineering,* on the subject of heat transfer, and the equipment that deals with it.

Here, in one volume, are the writings of fellow chemical engineers who also graduated with the basic understanding that Q = CAT and that heat-in equals heat-out. But they went on to specialize, and now they share with us their knowledge about the latest heat transfer equipment in today's chemical process industries.

This is where theory is put to the test: Boilers—how they work and how you can make them work better; Cooling—refrigeration, cooling towers, and chillers; Heating, insulation and winterizing; Condensers (with a calculator program); Dryers of all different sorts; and a pot pourri of other equipment, including fired heaters, fluidized beds, multistage evaporators and even solar ponds.

Life may not be so simple, but this book is going to make your life easier when it comes to heat transfer equipment. And so will the companion volume, which is geared to basic plant principles of heat transfer.

gas temperature of only 600 to 650°C instead of 1,000°C. Fig. 14 shows one of the largest boilers of this two-compartment design so far built.

The keys to success with this type of boiler are the adoption of a maximum heat-flux that is reasonable—having regard to the geometry and hydraulics of the boiler, the thorough understanding of the stresses in all parts of the boiler, the thermal protection of the inlet tubesheet, and the methods of attaching both the tube to the tubesheet, and the tubesheet to the shell and the channel.

Fig. 15 shows one successful design for dealing with the last three points, but various manufacturers have their own preferred ways of handling these problems. The author has a strong preference for the firetube-boiler design since it is far less sensitive to dirt or debris left in the system or released from the walls of the system during plant upsets. The presence of a 100 to 150-mm-thick layer of refractory inside the inlet channel results in a large "untubed" annulus on the shell side. Thus, a large amount of dirt or debris could accumulate in the base of the boiler without building up on the heat-transfer surface and without interfering with boiler circulation. This advantage disappears completely if the boiler is mounted vertically, and the author is strongly opposed to the use of vertical firetube boilers even if, as in some cases, they are attractive from the point of view of plant layout.

Of the watertube reformed-gas boilers that are built, the most common is the natural-circulation "bayonet-tube" design. This should not be taken as implying that it is the best boiler—it happens to be the design favored by the world's largest supplier of ammonia plants.

The principal features of this type of boiler are shown in Fig. 16 (left). Water from the steam drum enters the upper chamber and passes through the false tubesheet containing the bayonet tubes. At the bottom, it reverses and flows up through the annulus between the bayonet and scabbard tubes. The hot gas enters at the bottom of the vessel and flows across baffles, leaving at the top.

The proponents of this design point out that the central downcomer tube is not heated and that the steam bubbles generated are required to flow only upward. This is basically a sound argument, although the details on some plants have been such that reverse circulation has occurred under certain circumstances and this has sometimes led to failure.

There are others who argue that the vertical U-tube boiler, Fig. 16 (center) used on many plants is equally satisfactory, particularly when circulation is ensured by the use of forced-circulation pumps. They also argue that the whole boiler duty can be achieved in a single exchanger, whereas in the other design the bayonet-tube boiler is followed by a firetube boiler. Several boilermakers have made two or three of their own designs of watertube reformed-gas boilers, incorporating features that have special merit but that often add to the cost and complexity of the units—Fig. 16 (right), 17 and 18.

Perhaps the one of most technical interest is the mono-tube boiler installed on a 1,000-t/d ammonia plant in France, shown in Fig. 19 and 20. This generates 137 t/h of steam at 152 bar in a single vessel. The installation is the most striking that the author has seen. The main reasons are that there is no large steam drum and associated structure, only a vertical separator that is little more than a pipe attached to the boiler; there are no risers or downcomers; there are no circulating pumps; the whole duty is handled inside one shell; and temperature control is achieved by an internal arrangement, thus avoiding hot-gas piping. Further details are given by Silberring [11].

The fact that this boiler has operated without trouble for five years does not imply that it is the most reliable watertube boiler—it is more a tribute to the quality of control of the plant and particularly of the water. Nevertheless, most of the watertube reformed-gas boilers known to the writer have low points (where any debris can collect) in the zones of highest heat flux, thus giving rise to the risk of corrosion or overheating of the type described in Ref. 4. Furthermore, they are all likely to fail if poor precommissioning or a plant upset causes a significant flow blockage at the inlet of one or more tubes. Notwithstanding these potential risks, some users have had reliable service from watertube boilers.

There is a significant point in favor of most designs of watertube boilers. Inadequate water-treatment can lead to the rapid failure of the tubes of either a watertube or a firetube boiler. In a watertube type, if a large number of tubes fail, a spare watertube bundle can be fitted in quite a short time, whereas a firetube boiler would require a very long time to retube or replace. Such major failures are rare, and if only a few tubes are affected they can be readily plugged off with either design.

Steam drums

The main purpose of a steam drum is to separate the steam from the steam/water mixtures that return from a boiler, but it also provides a holdup capacity of water to feed the boilers. In forced-circulation watertube boilers, the ratio of the quantity of water circulating to that

Layers of suitable ceramic paper wrapped in continuous roll

Protection plate (optional)   Concrete   Ferrule machined to ensure good fit in tube when operating

Some key features of firetube boiler   Fig. 15

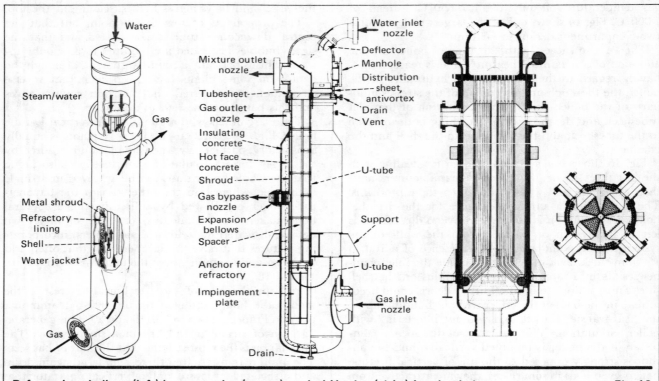

Reformed-gas boilers: (left) bayonet-tube, (center) vertical U-tube, (eight) Lentjes design   Fig. 16

which is converted into steam may be as low as 4 to 1, whereas in a natural-circulation firetube boiler it is normally between 10 to 1 and 20 to 1.

Thus, the primary stage of separation is the coarse one of removing the bulk of the water from the steam. The second stage is the removal of water droplets from the steam. This stage is of vital importance if the steam is subsequently to be superheated and used in turbines. The dissolved solids in the feedwater concentrate up to a hundredfold in the boiler water, depending on the amount of blowdown or purge from the system. As a result, any boiler water carried over in the steam contains a high level of dissolved solids.

The solids will be deposited in the superheater. Some solids will build up on the heat-transfer surfaces, resulting in overheating and even possibly creep rupture failure. Some may deposit in the turbine and cause a lowering of efficiency. The most serious event that can occur is "priming" of the steam drum when there is bulk carryover of water due to a plant upset or loss of control. Not only does this have a severe effect on the superheaters but it can lead to failure of the steam turbines.

A common design figure in many boiler specifications is that the steam drum shall have a separation efficiency of 99%. This has little meaning; it cannot be measured, and—even if it were achieved—it would be completely inadequate for most high-pressure boilers fitted with superheaters. It is better to state that the steam leaving the drum shall have a solids content of less than, say, 0.01 ppm of sodium.

An isokinetic sample point should be provided in the steam line from the drum. This should be connected to a continuous analyzer fitted with high-level alarms. Such a purity level usually can only be achieved in the sophisticated steam drums developed by leading boiler-makers. Fig. 21 shows such a drum, in which the primary separation is carried out in a large number of small cyclones, and the final separation in packs of chevron pads. Knitted wiremesh pads are sometimes used and these are equally acceptable, but the author is very suspicious of those who claim that the guaranteed

Fabricated tube-bundle of Lentjes boiler   Fig. 17

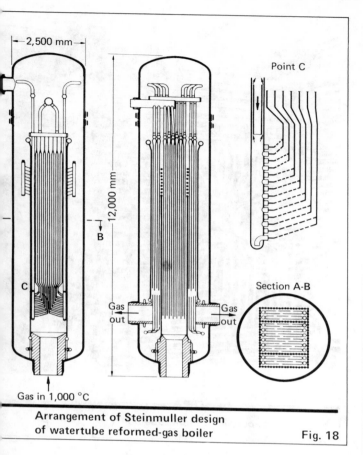

Arrangement of Steinmuller design of watertube reformed-gas boiler   Fig. 18

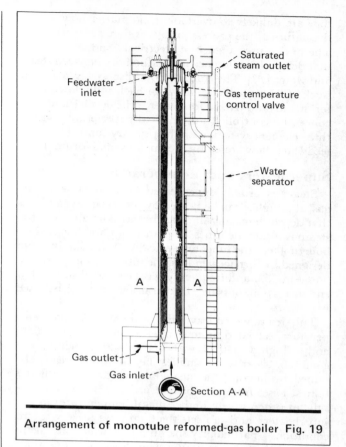

Arrangement of monotube reformed-gas boiler   Fig. 19

purity can be achieved with simple baffles inside an ordinary pressure vessel.

Additional advantages accrue from the use of a specialist boilermaker's steam drum. He usually has developed special designs for the uniform distribution of chemicals for water treatment, for the uniform removal of blowdown water, and for the design of the downcomers to ensure that there is no underflow of the steam that could either upset the circulation of the system or cause cavitation in boiler circulation pumps. Nevertheless, experience shows that close liaison is necessary with the boilermaker to ensure that the standard design is modified where necessary to take account of any differences that arise in process waste-heat-boiler systems.

In one particular case, the boilermaker had selected the number of cyclones appropriate to the evaporation rate of his watertube boilers and had completely overlooked the fact that with the natural-circulation firetube boilers, the quantity of water returning with the steam was several times greater. Not only were the cyclones seriously overloaded but the chambers enclosing the riser outlets were damaged, nuts came loose, and carryover occurred on a massive scale.

Another problem that occurred and caused failures was reverse circulation in one or more boilers sharing a common steam drum. This had arisen because one of the boilers in the process was brought on load earlier than the others. The normal practice, of allowing all risers to enter a common equalized chamber, had been followed, and, as a consequence of this, the hydraulic head generated in the operating boiler had been suffi-

cient to initiate reverse circulation in the cold boiler.

This incident should not be taken as a reason for discontinuing the highly desirable practice of one common drum. The boilermaker, when made aware of the circumstances, can arrange the baffles to avoid the problem, albeit at the expense of some extra cyclones.

An important aspect of the steam drum concerns the maintenance of drum level. If the size of the steam drum is arrived at on the basis of providing adequate space for the steam purity equipment, then the holdup capacity between the normal drum level and that of the drum empty (i.e., exposed downcomer entry) may be only one or two minutes. This is probably inadequate when one bears in mind the many factors that demand the attention of the plant operators during the upset of a complex process plant.

In nitric acid plants, this is not a serious problem since the unit can be automatically tripped out before the level becomes dangerously low. However, in reforming plants, there is large heat capacity in the system, and flow through the reformers must continue in order to protect the catalyst. In these cases, more holdup capacity is desirable, and process contractors usually provide at least three minutes capacity—users that have suffered boiler failures caused by loss of level sometimes specify five minutes. The cost of this extra capacity is not insignificant for large plants.

An instrument for indicating water level, which has recently become available, is worthy of special mention, since it provides the operators in the control room with such a vivid indication of the steam drum level that they are unlikely to overlook it, no matter how serious the nature of the process problems they are faced with. The device uses a stack of electrical conductivity cells that detect the difference in conductivity between steam and water [13]. The control room display has a similar stack of 20-mm-square lights for each cell, glowing red for steam and green for water. The level should, of course, be controlled automatically, preferably with a three-element system, with the primary control being of feedwater flow, reset by steam flow and drum level.

Superheaters and attemperators

Steam is usually superheated by contact with flue gas, although it can be heated by process gases in plants that do not have any flue gas. In virtually all cases, the steam is inside the tubes. In plants that are designed by boilermakers, the tubes are typically $1\frac{1}{2}$ in. dia. In those designed by furnace vendors, the tubes are more usually 3 to 4 in. dia. and frequently have extended surfaces to enhance the outside heat-transfer coefficient (see Fig. 5).

The steam, which leaves the drum at saturation temperature, is heated up to temperatures as low as 300°C and as high as 540°C, with 460 to 480°C being more common. Clearly, the smallest heat-transfer area is obtained by heating the steam in counterflow with the hottest gases from the furnace or the reactor. This results in progressively higher metal temperatures in the superheaters, and subjects the final rows to very severe conditions—particularly the final two, which are likely to receive heat by radiation as well as by convection.

The tubes in such a superheater are vulnerable to creep-rupture failure due to overheating, if the gases are hotter than expected or if the steam flow is less than expected or if there are transient operational modes in which there is a mismatch between the flue-gas rate and the rate of steam production. In some designs, an attempt is made to minimize these effects by the insertion of one or two rows of evaporator tubes to shield the superheater.

The approach preferred by the author, for plants in which the risks described above are real, is shown in Fig. 22. The superheating duty is divided between a primary superheater and secondary superheater. The former, which heats the saturated steam from the drum, is in normal counterflow. The secondary superheater is in cocurrent flow with the hotter flue gas.

In cases where the computer simulations referred to earlier show that the steam temperature would still vary excessively under certain operating conditions, an attemperator can be installed to control the steam outlet temperature by cooling part of the steam from the primary superheater in the manner shown in Fig. 22. This is most easily accomplished in a drum attemperator, which consists of heat-exchanger bundles situated in the water space of the steam drum. A controlled amount of steam is cooled by evaporating water in the drum.

Notwithstanding the above precautions, it is the view of the author that for design purposes an additional margin of say 50°C should be provided on top of the predicted long-term metal temperature in order to cover unforeseen happenings, such as solids carryover

Fabricated tube-bundle of monotube boiler   **Fig. 20**

from the drum, stratification of hot gas, or some of the other happenings described in the foregoing section on steam drums. This margin is not sacrosanct and should be reviewed if, for example, it leads to a very large increase in cost by requiring a change from ferritic to austenitic steel.

This general approach to the design of superheaters should also be applied to any process heaters that are included in the flue-gas duct.

Combustion-air heaters

Brief mention must be made of combustion-air heaters, since they are a common feature of flue-gas streams of waste-heat-boiler systems. If the fuel is natural gas, then no problems should be expected, and the user can install an air preheater of the type shown in Fig. 6. For large plants, the capital cost of the air preheater can be reduced significantly by using the rotary type, but this saving has to be balanced against the slightly increased risk of unreliability brought about by the introduction of moving parts and the additional running costs arising from air leakage across the seals. Another alternative that warrants an economic evaluation is a design that uses internally and externally finned cast-iron tubes. The various alternatives are described, illustrated and discussed in Ref 15. A relatively new entry not covered in that review is a design based on the use of heat pipes.

If the fuel contains sulfur, more care is required. Glass tubing has been successfully used in the coldest passes of tubular air heaters. In the case of rotary air heaters, a

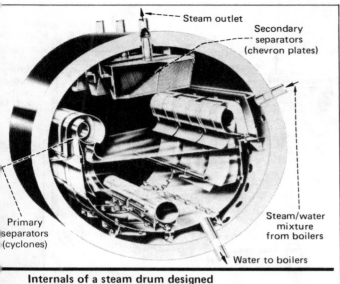

Internals of a steam drum designed
to produce steam of high purity   Fig. 21

small steam-heated suction is often used to preheat the inlet air by the amount necessary to keep the main heater above the acid dewpoint.

Forced- and induced-draft fans

Induced-draft fans are installed on virtually all modern furnaces. In many cases, in order to achieve maximum heat recovery, the combustion air is preheated by the flue gas, and a forced-draft fan is required to overcome the pressure losses in the combustion-air preheater and in the burner windbox.

Many of the earlier plants incorporating such equipment had their outputs limited by the capacity of the forced- or induced-draft fans. The burners may have required more air to achieve their duty. Furthermore, that duty may have been underestimated. Consequently, the forced-draft fan could not supply that amount of air without being increased in size. The problem was often worse in the case of the induced-draft fan because the additional quantity of flue gas was increased still further by air leakage into the furnace and its convection section.

Clearly, it is desirable to introduce some margins, and the author advocates a figure of 10 to 20% on the forced-draft fan rate and 15 to 25% on the induced-draft fan rate. It is important when specifying the fan duty to ensure that this increased flow is achieved with pressure losses appropriate to the increased flow. This, of course, leads to a much larger driver, and it may be economic to supply a variable-speed drive, or inlet guide vanes, on the fans to minimize the power consumption should the plant not need the margins built into them.

Obviously, introduction of the fans could lead to a decrease in plant reliability. In the opinion of the author, reliability is best obtained by installing one high-quality fan rather than by duplicating ordinary fans.

Mechanical design and fabrication

It is inappropriate here to discuss the detailed mechanical design and fabrication of each of the many items of equipment in a complex waste-heat-boiler system but their importance should not be underestimated. The author [1,4] has highlighted costly failures that have arisen as a result of poor detailed design and bad workmanship. Frequently, companies use their best engineers to perform the conceptual and basic design and then pass on the execution of the contract without managing to convey the importance and requirement of the plant for special quality.

The client should take steps to ensure that this does not happen. Prior to the order, he or his main contractor should lay down procedures for submission for approval of detailed designs, welding procedures, quality-control schedules, manufacturing procedures, protection and shipping instructions. Also, he or the contractor should arrange to supplement the internal inspection by external inspection, as appropriate. These comments apply equally well to onsite fabrication, where there is probably even greater need for continuous scrutiny of the quality of workmanship including, in particular, the welding.

Precommissioning of waste-heat-boiler systems

Objective

The objective of the precommissioning is to ensure that when the boiler system goes into service, it is free from debris, scale and corrosive products, and that all the metal surfaces are covered with a uniform tightly adhered layer of magnetite. It is desirable that the feedwater system be cleaned in a similar manner, to prevent the carrying of scale and debris into the steam-generation circuits.

Provision for cleaning at the design stage

The general approach to the cleaning processes should be set at a very early stage, so that the design of the equipment and piping that are to be cleaned incorporates the required piping connections, as well as access for inspection and physical removal of debris. All too often, this is not the case. Then, late and costly alterations are made to the piping, and undesirable compromises are accepted.

Piping connections should be provided and sized to achieve an optimum cleaning velocity over the heat-transfer surfaces (e.g., about 0.3 m/s for 5% hydrochloric acid solution). Where there are several boilers in parallel, provision may have to be made for cleaning each boiler separately.

The total system to be cleaned should be critically examined to establish where dirt and debris will collect during cleaning, and provision should be made for its physical removal. In the case of firetube boilers, the blowdown pipes in the bottom annulus can be attached to a removable pad. For some watertube boilers, a "mud pot" can be provided on the bottom of the distribution manifolds.

Cleanliness during construction

Equipment should be supplied in a clean dry condition, and in some cases shipping under a blanket of nitrogen is justified. Those involved in construction should be aware of the need to take special care over cleanliness. They should understand that if they were to leave behind only one foreign body it could, during operation, restrict the flow of water and cause a boiler failure (particularly if the boiler is of watertube design). Prefabricated sections of piping for the system should be cleaned mechanically to remove mill scale. Wire-brushing, even by power tools, is seldom a satisfactory method of descaling, but high-pressure water jets can remove a significant proportion of the scale. Alternatively, grit blasting can be used.

Cleanliness is an important aspect of inspection of equipment (1) prior to dispatch from the manufacturer's works, (2) after the equipment is received on site, and, (3) during inspection of the whole system prior to hand-over to the commissioning staff.

Planning the chemical cleaning procedure

A detailed plan of the cleaning procedure must be drawn up and agreed upon between the cleaning contractor and client, and there must be supervisors from both parties who know every detail of the programs. A careful check should be made to ensure that the pumps that the contractor proposes to use can achieve the rate corresponding to the optimum cleaning velocity, taking into account the resistance in the circuits. A suitable spare pump must always be available.

Cleaning operations

A typical procedure for the chemical cleaning of an important system operating under arduous conditions is outlined below.

Stage 1. Flush out to remove loose material. Use a water velocity equal to or greater than that which will occur in service.

Stage 2. Alkaline-degrease for 24 h at 95 to 100°C, using 1,000 to 1,500 ppm by weight of trisodium phosphate and a suitable detergent.

Stage 3. Acid-clean using 5% inhibited hydrochloric acid at 75 to 85°C. Continue until the total iron content in the circulating system has reached a definite plateau, typically 0.3 to 0.4 g/L.

Stage 4. Citric-acid flush using a 0.2% solution.

Stage 5. Passivate using ammoniated hydrazine solution at 95 to 100°C for 24 h.

Stage 6. Drain system and dry thoroughly.

In the case of the plant illustrated in Fig. 6, a special step was introduced between Stages 2 and 3. For nearly two days, water was circulated while tests were carried out to check, by contact flowmeter [14], that each of the membrane tubes in the auxiliary boiler had a similar flowrate and, particularly, that none of the tubes was blocked.

Storage

If the boiler system is not held under the correct conditions after cleaning, much of the passivation can be lost within a few days. The system can be stored wet (if filled with ammoniated hydrazine solution) or dry (using dehumidified air or nitrogen). The use of dehumidified air allows access to the system for further work or inspection, without costly, time-consuming purging and drying.

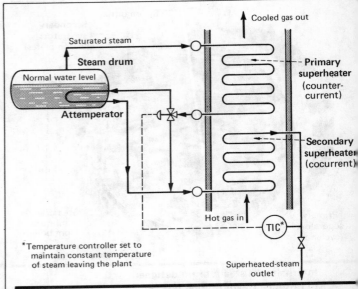

Superheater system that maintains constant outlet steam temperature; holds down metal temperatures   Fig. 22

Conclusions

The general approach and techniques described above have been developed as a result of dealing with the problems of earlier plants.

Striking success with large new plants demonstrates that high-temperature, high-pressure waste-heat-boiler systems can be incorporated into process plants without introducing significant risk of unreliability. These plants were designed taking into account the principal factors listed below as recommendations.

For the system as a whole:

Development of a process flowsheet should be done in close consultation with experienced engineering specialists who can influence the choice of steam conditions and the positioning of items of equipment in the flowstreams, in order to ensure that they are able to design and purchase reliable equipment.

A computer model of the system should be developed that can predict the duty of each item of equipment under startup, part-load and trip conditions, as well as under normal conditions.

The supplier of the equipment should be made aware of special aspects of particular problems, the chief of these being potential corrosion problems and the choice of materials of construction.

The supplier should be told of the need for high standards in detailed design, manufacture and quality control in the works and on site, and arrangements should be made for the monitoring of these matters to the extent judged appropriate for each particular case.

Special attention should be given to the precommissioning procedures, including mechanical cleaning and various chemical-treatment stages. The basic approach should be agreed upon at a very early stage, so that the design of the equipment and piping that are to be cleaned incorporates the required piping connections and access for inspection and the physical removal of debris.

The quality of the feedwater and return condensate

should be continuously monitored, and automatic trips should be installed in certain locations, in order to prevent contaminated water entering the treated-water storage tank or deaerator.

For individual items of equipment:

Undeaerated-boiler-feedwater heaters—Special care should be given to the choice of materials of construction, particularly with regard to the risk of corrosion on both sides of the tubes.

If possible, the heating fluid should be at a lower pressure than the feedwater, if leakage of the former could introduce harmful chemicals into the boiler.

Deaerators—The design should be very critically examined in view of the significant quantity of oxygen entering as a result of the high proportion of fresh makeup water in process plant systems.

The design of the system should ensure that, under all conditions, the amount of steam in the deaerator is sufficient for scrubbing out the oxygen.

The design of the deaerator should be such as to minimize the vibration arising from the introduction of heating steam and hot condensate.

Boiler-feedwater heaters/economizers—The risk of steaming should be assessed, and if this is considered likely, an appropriate design should be adopted.

The danger of "acid dewpoint" corrosion should be assessed, and if this is considered likely, a special design should be used.

Waste-heat boilers heated by flue gas—Where possible, vertical natural-circulation boilers should be used, and if horizontal boilers are essential, the design should be checked to ensure that "dryout" does not occur at the crown of the tubes.

Waste-heat boilers heated by process gas—Whenever possible, proprietary boilers should be selected that have evolved with the process and have become established as reliable. When this is not the case, the choice of type of boiler and of fabricator warrants most careful consideration, bearing in mind that the cost of failures has often exceeded the cost of the boiler. Horizontal natural-circulation firetube boilers have much to commend them, provided that the vendor is very knowledgeable in their design and fabrication. Nevertheless, a number of good designs of watertube boilers exist and have been used with success on plants where special care has been taken to remove debris from the system.

Steam drums—The sophisticated steam drums evolved by leading boilermakers should be used on systems with high-temperature superheaters, and severe standards should be enforced on the maximum level of contaminants permitted in the steam.

When several boilers share the same drum, its internal baffles should be so arranged as to ensure that reverse circulation is not initiated in any of the boilers.

Water storage capacity should be provided appropriate to the heat capacity of the equipment.

Superheaters—For severe-duty superheaters, the design should incorporate selected features that minimize the actual metal temperatures and maintain close control of steam outlet temperatures over all operating conditions.

The mechanical design should include an additional temperature margin to overcome unpredictable increases in metal temperatures.

Forced- and induced-draft fans—The duty specified should include a generous margin to ensure that the fans do not limit the plant output. Robust reliable machines should be selected.

Acknowledgements

The author wishes to acknowledge and thank the many people who, over the years, have contributed a great deal of information, help and advice on the matters discussed in this paper. They include numerous colleagues and designers, fabricators and operators from many parts of the world. Thanks are also due to vendors who provided several of the illustrations used in this article.

Illustration credits

The following companies supplied illustrative material for this article: Borsig, Fig. 11, 12; CCM-Sulzer, Fig. 19, 20; Foster Wheeler, Fig. 21; Oschutz, Fig. 8; Pullman Kellogg, Fig. 16 (left); S.H.G., Fig. 10; Steinmuller, Fig. 7, 9, 13, 14, 18; Struthers Wells, Fig. 16 (center).

References

1. Hinchley, P., Waste Heat Boilers in the Chemical Industry, paper presented at Institution of Mechanical Engineers Conference on "Energy Recovery in Process Plants," Jan. 29–31, 1975 and subsequently published in *Chem. Eng.*, Sept. 1, 1975, pp. 94–98.
2. Appl, P., and Frink, K., Troubles with Thin Tube Sheet Waste Heat Boilers, AIChE 1975 Ammonia Plant Safety, Vol. 18, pp. 113–121.
3. Sawyer, J. G., others, Causes of Shut Downs in Ammonia Plants, AIChE Safety in Air and Ammonia Plants, Vol. 14, pp. 61–68 and Vol. 16, pp. 4–9.
4. Hinchley, P., Waste Heat Boilers: Problems and Solutions, *Chem. Eng. Prog.*, Mar. 1977, pp. 90–96.
5. Strauss, S. D., Water Treatment, *Power*, June 1973.
6. Neue Richtlinien fur das Kesselspeisewasser und das Kesselwasser von Dampferzeugern, VGB Kraftwerkstechnik, No. 2–52, Apr. 1972, pp. 167–172.
7. Becker, J., Examples for the Design of Heat Exchangers in Chemical Plant, *Verfahrenstechnik*, Vol. 3, No. 8, pp. 335–350 (1969).
8. Kummel, V. J., Abhitze and Sonderkessel in der chemischen und petrochemischen Industrie, *Chem-Ing-Tech.*, Vol. 49 No. 6,5, pp. 475–479 (1977).
9. Capitaine, D., and Stoffels, Jentzsch, Der Einsatz von Abhitzekesseln and einige Konstructionsmerksmale, *Mitteilungen der VGB*, Vol. 49, No. 3, July 1969, pp. 165–173.
10. Deuse, K. H., Waste Heat Boilers in Large Plants, *Het Ingenieursblad*, 40E Jaargang (1971), No. 21.
11. Silberring, L., Waste Heat Recovery in Ammonia Plants, CPE—Heat Transfer Survey 1969, and Energetische Probleme der Ammoniak—Erzeugung, *Chem-Ing-Tech*, Vol. 43, January 1971, No. 12, pp. 711–720.
12. Knulle, H. R., Problems with Exchangers in Ethylene Plants, *Chem. Eng. Prog.*, Vol. 68, No. 7, pp. 53–56 (1972).
13. Hasler, E. F., and Martin, R. E., Hydrastep: a 'Fail Operative' Gauge System to replace Visual Boiler Water Level Gauges, *Measurement and Control*, Dec. 1971, pp. 366–371.
14. Roughton, J. E., Detection of Boiler Tube Blockages. Experience with CERL Contract Flowmeter, *CEBG Digest*, May, 1973, pp. 7–10.
15. Berman, H. L., Fired Heaters—IV, How to reduce your fuel bill, *Chem. Eng.*, Sept. 11, 1978, pp. 165–169.

The author

Peter Hinchley works in Project Management for the Agricultural Div., Imperial Chemical Industries Ltd., P.O. Box 6, Billingham, Cleveland TS23 1LD, England. For almost ten years he was manager of the Furnace & Boiler section, where he had extensive experience in design, specification and purchasing of waste-heat boilers. He holds a first-class Honors degree in mechanical engineering from Sheffield University and is a Member of the Institution of Mechanical Engineers.

Retrofitting coal-fired boilers: economics for process plants

After investigating the economics of installing coal-fired boilers in existing plants, this article offers guidance on conditions for profitable investments. It also examines the consequences of tighter pollution regulations and the maturing of fluidized-bed technology.

C. Thomas Breuer, Arthur D. Little, Inc.

☐ New coal-fired boilers appear economically attractive as an alternative to oil- and gas-fired boilers in many U.S. chemical process plants. Uncertainties in federal natural-gas policies and in future supplies and prices of fuel oil can also make coal the preferred fuel for meeting large, steady demands for process steam.

About 60% of the fuel consumed in the chemical process industries (CPI) is estimated to be burned in boilers. Coal and miscellaneous fuels (principally, process wastes) amount to about 27%. Oil and natural gas account for the remainder. Thus, there is significant potential for displacing oil and natural gas with coal.

Basis of the analysis

It is assumed in this analysis that existing gas-fired-boiler capacity is adequate to fill all of a plant's steam demands. It is further assumed that the gas-fired boiler will be kept in working condition, capable of filling in for the coal-fired boiler and meeting demand for steam that exceeds the latter's capacity.

The focus is on CPI plants in which steam demand is high enough for the installation of a coal-fired boiler having a nameplate firing rate of between 75 and 250 million Btu/h. This size range is chosen for two reasons:

1. The steam supply economics are transitional. There are many plants in which steam demand may be most economically supplied by one of three types of coal-fired boilers that will be evaluated in this article. But there are others for which oil or gas will continue to be the most economical fuel.

The economics of coal are neither compelling (as is often the case with boilers fired with more than 250 million Btu/h of fuel) nor prohibitive (as is generally the case with boilers fired with less than 75 million Btu/h). Within this transition range, enlightening comparisons can be made among the different boiler technologies, and an examination of the comparisons is possible with regard to regional differences in prospective energy prices.

2. State regulations on emissions of air pollutants apply to boilers in this size range. Although these regulations vary, they are generally less strict than the federal New Source Performance Standards applicable to larger boilers. The implications of possible federal air pollution regulations on boilers in this size range will be considered, as well as the full commercialization of the fluidized-bed boiler, with its potential for superior pollution control.

Financial and tax parameters

All costs in this analysis are in 1982 constant dollars. Therefore, only real changes in fuel and other operating and maintenance costs over the life of the system need be of concern. Unless otherwise specified, the values of the financial parameters are:

Useful life—20 yr; the consequences of variations in return on equity are described.

Debt/equity ratio—30/70; this is typical for large U.S. companies.

Real interest rate—3.5%; this is appropriate for a constant-dollar analysis.

Property tax rate—2%.

Corporate tax rate—50%; this includes federal and state rates.

Depreciation life—5 yr; by the accelerated cost recovery system.

Inflation rate—8%; this is required only for calculating tax depreciation, because the analysis otherwise is based on constant dollars.

Investment tax credit—10%.

Texas fuel prices are used for the base-case projection, and Alabama and Illinois prices for the alternative projections (Table I). These 1982 constant-dollar prices are based on U.S. Dept. of Energy projections, allowing for the discounted effects of real-price increases through the year 2005.

Options in coal-fired boilers

Summarized in Table II are the key characteristics of the principal commercially available coal-fired boilers. The following options are considered:

■ Stoker-fired boiler burning compliance coal.

Originally published September 17, 1984

18

small expenditure at the time of initial purchase will yield significant returns when calculated over the boiler's entire life.

One of the most common reasons for poor efficiency is excess combustion air. Theoretically, in order to burn all of the fuel, a specific (stoichiometric) quantity of air is required. When more than this theoretical amount is used, energy is wasted in heating the excess air. However, to guarantee complete combustion and prevent smoke formation, even the most efficient boilers must operate with some excess air. About 10 to 20% excess air offers a good compromise between safety, efficiency and pollution control. Excess air is regulated by the proper adjustment of combustion controls, coupled with flue-gas analysis.

Low-excess-air burners are now available that can yield significant energy savings. Due to its mechanical design, a low-excess-air burner can use much less air than the normal packaged boiler. The term "low excess air" is applied to burners that require only 5% excess air or less. Another benefit of the low-excess-air burner is that its use can result in lower stack-emissions and lower NO_x design capability.

Combustion control systems

Combustion control systems for packaged boilers range from the simple to the very sophisticated. It is a mistake to automatically assume that there is an economic payout of energy savings from investing in the more-sophisticated systems. It is not unusual for such a system to cost $60,000, or more, while saving only a few thousand dollars.

A combustion-control system generally serves two functions: setting the fuel/air ratio, and maintaining load. Generally speaking, there are two approaches to achieving combustion control: using positioning control (the simplified system) and using metering control (more sophisticated).

A positioning-control system can be either on/off, high/low/off, or modulating positioning. In the modulating-positioning control system, the air and fuel control-valve settings are continuously varied. Both settings are determined by the steam load on the boiler. The typical CPI packaged boiler can use positioning control via mechanical linkages, or control rods, which are connected to the fuel valves and air damper.

The more-sophisticated metering system can be either semi-metering or full-metering. For the full-metering system, one input (either fuel or air) is controlled according to load. The flow of the other input is measured and controlled according to the measured flow of the first input. Normally, this sophisticated system can only be justified when there are simultaneous multiple fuel firings, variable fuel properties, or use of multiple burners.

Automatic oxygen-trim control is a popular method, based on the measured oxygen levels in the exhaust, for trimming the level of air fed to the boiler. It can be applied to either the positioning system or the metering system.

However, it is not unusual to discover that, by analyzing the distribution of the operating time versus the load ranges, oxygen-trim control does not have an energy-savings payout. It is a common mistake to retrofit existing systems with oxygen-trim control based on a false analysis of savings. The false justification for such control results from comparing a poorly tuned existing control system with the proposed oxygen-trim system. Often, one can take the existing control system—whatever shape it is in—and achieve significant savings by reducing the excess air by proper tuning of the system load characteristics. Such savings can be maintained by regular monitoring of the boiler efficiency. Properly, one should compare the proposed oxygen-trim control system to the best that the present control system can achieve.

Using economizers

The typical CPI packaged boiler can achieve an annual savings of 3% by installing an economizer that preheats the boiler feedwater by using waste heat from the flue gas. In general, a 1% increase in efficiency can be obtained by decreasing the flue-gas temperature by 40°F, thereby raising the boiler feedwater temperature by 10°F.

An economizer is justifiable only if there is inadequate heat-transfer surface in the boiler to remove sufficient heat given off by the flame. However, due to the typical sizing of the packaged boiler, it is not unusual to find that an economizer is justifiable. Remember that with conventional economizers, there is a minimum flue-gas temperature required to avoid corrosion. This temperature depends upon the fuel used and the economizer design. For natural gas, the minimum temperature is generally 250°F; for No. 2 fuel oil, 275°F; and for high-sulfur oils, 320°F.

By atomizing fuel oil with air, rather than with steam, an average annual energy saving of 1% can be achieved, because more energy is required to produce steam than to produce compressed air. Steam atomization usually requires 1% of the energy in the fuel, versus a fraction of a percent for air.

Summary

The CPI packaged boiler often has a shorter-than-expected life and is less efficient than anticipated. Proper boiler specifications, written prior to purchase, can overcome these deficiencies. Implementation of the corrosion resistance and energy recommendations given in this article will ensure extended boiler life and good energy efficiency.

The author

Charles W. Hawk, Jr., is a project manager of Olin Corp.'s Southeast Regional Engineering group, P.O. Box 248, Charleston, TN 37310; (615) 336-4360. He has been responsible for engineering on several capital projects at Olin's chlor/alkali plants. He was previously a maintenance engineer at Olin's Augusta, Ga., plant. His prior experience was with Procter & Gamble and Martin Marietta. He holds a B.S. in mechanical engineering from the University of Tennessee, has had one patent issued and has several pending, and is a registered professional engineer in Georgia, Alabama and Tennessee.

Boiler heat recovery

To minimize fuel costs, heat can be recovered from both flue gases and boiler blowdown.

William G. Moran and *Guillermo H. Hoyos,**
Engineering Experiment Station,
Georgia Institute of Technology

☐ Boiler flue gases are rejected to the stack at temperatures at least 100 to 150°F higher than the temperature of the generated steam. Obviously, recovering a portion of this heat will result in higher boiler efficiencies and reduced fuel consumption.

Heat recovery can be accomplished by using either an economizer to heat the water feedstream or an air preheater for the combustion air. Normally, adding an economizer is preferable to installing an air preheater on an existing boiler, although air preheaters should be given careful consideration in new installations.

Economizers are available that can be economically retrofitted to boilers as small as 100 hp (3,450 lb/h steam produced).

Fig. 1 can be used to estimate the amount of heat that can be recovered from flue gases. Two main assumptions have been made in developing this graph:

1. The boiler operates close to optimum excess-air levels. (It does not make sense to use an expensive heat-recovery system to correct for inefficiencies caused by improper boiler tuneup.)

2. The lowest temperature to which the flue gases can be cooled depends on the type of fuel used: 250°F for natural gas, 300°F for coal and low-sulfur-content fuel oils, and 350°F for high-sulfur-content fuel oils.

These limits are set by the flue-gas dewpoint, or by cold-end corrosion, or heat driving-force considerations.

Example

A boiler generates 45,000 lb/h of 150-psig steam by burning a No. 2 fuel oil that has a 1% sulfur content. Some of the condensate is returned to the boiler and mixed with fresh water to yield a 117°F boiler feed. The stack temperature is measured at 550°F.

Determine the annual savings (assuming 8,400 h/yr boiler operation) that will be achieved by installing an economizer in the stack.

Assume that fuel energy costs $3/million Btu.

*This material has been prepared by staff members of Georgia Tech's Industrial Energy Extension Service, which is a continuing energy-conservation program funded by the State of Georgia Office of Energy Resources.

Originally published December 3, 1979

Babcock & Wilcox Ltd.

From steam tables, the following heat values are available:

For 150°F saturated steam   1,195.50 Btu/lb
For 117°F feedwater   84.97 Btu/lb

The boiler heat output is calculated as follows:

$$\text{Output} = 45,000(1,195.50 - 84.97)$$
$$= 50 \text{ million Btu/lb.}$$

Using the curve for low-sulfur-content oils, the heat recovered that corresponds to a stack temperature of

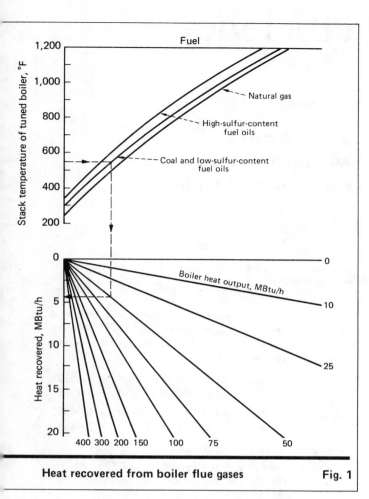

Heat recovered from boiler flue gases   Fig. 1

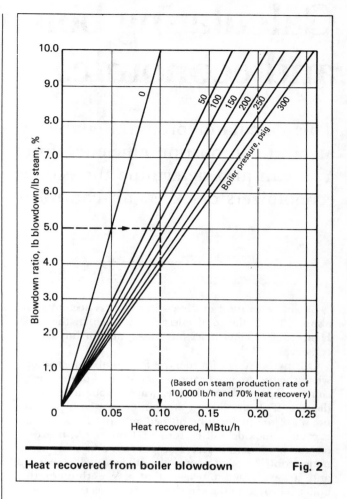

Heat recovered from boiler blowdown   Fig. 2

550°F and a boiler duty of 50 million Btu/h can be read from the graph as 4.3 million Btu/h. The annual savings are:

4.3 MBtu/h × $3/MBtu × 8,400 h/yr = $108,000/yr

Recovering heat from boiler blowdown

Heat can also be recovered from boiler blowdown, by preheating the boiler makeup water through use of a heat exchanger. This is done most conveniently in continuous-blowdown systems.

Example

In a plant where the cost of steam is $2.50/MBtu, 1,250 lb/h are continuously purged in order to avoid buildup of solids in the boiler tubes. Determine the yearly savings (assume 8,760 h of operation per year) if the blowdown is passed through a heat exchanger to raise the temperature of the makeup water. The boiler generates 125-psig steam at a rate of 25,000 lb/h.

First calculate the blowdown ratio:

$$\text{Blowdown ratio} = \frac{1{,}250 \text{ lb/h blowdown}}{25{,}000 \text{ lb/h steam}} = 5\%$$

From Fig. 2, the heat recovered, corresponding to 5% blowdown ratio and 125-psig boiler pressure, is 0.100 MBtu/h.

Since Fig. 2 is based on a steam production rate of 10,000 lb/h, the actual yearly savings for this plant are:

Savings:

$$= 0.100 \frac{\text{MBtu}}{\text{h}} \times \frac{25{,}000 \text{ lb/h}}{10{,}000 \text{ lb/h}} \times 8{,}760 \frac{\text{h}}{\text{yr}} \times \frac{\$2.5}{\text{MBtu}}$$

$$= \$5{,}500$$

The values obtained from Fig. 2 are based on a makeup water temperature of 70°F and a heat recovery of 70%.

Suggested actions

Determine stack temperature after boiler has been carefully tuned up. Then determine minimum temperature to which stack gases can be cooled and study economics of installing an economizer or air preheater. Also study savings from installing a heat exchanger on blowdown.

The authors

William G. Moran is a research engineer at the Engineering Experiment Station, Georgia Institute of Technology, Atlanta, GA 30332. His present fields of interest include industrial and commercial energy conservation, alternative energy sources, and research and development. He holds a B.S. from the University of Massachusetts and an M.S. from Rensselaer Polytechnic Institute, both in mechanical engineering, and is a registered professional engineer in Georgia.
Guillermo H. Hoyos was a research engineer with Georgia Tech's Engineering Experiment Station when these materials were prepared. He holds B.S. and M.S. degrees in chemical engineering from Georgia Institute of Technology. He now resides in Bogota, Colombia.

Calculating boiler efficiency and economics

This calculator program enables you to figure excess
air and combustion efficiency from Orsat-apparatus readings.
You can also determine the economic advantages of adding
economizers or excess-air-control instrumentation.

Terry A. Stoa, ADM Corn Sweeteners

Steam generation in direct-fired boilers accounts for
about 50% of the total energy consumed in the U.S.
Hence, boiler efficiencies have a significant impact on
conservation [1].

During burning of a fuel, perfect combustion occurs
when the fuel/oxygen ratio is such that all of the fuel is
converted to carbon dioxide, water vapor and sulfur
dioxide. If an insufficient amount of oxygen is present,
not all of the fuel will be burned, and products such as
carbon monoxide will be formed. Conversely, if excess
oxygen is present, it serves no purpose and is in fact a
major contributor to poor boiler efficiency. The oxygen
and its associated nitrogen that passes through the
boiler is heated to the same temperature as the combustion products. This heating uses energy that would
otherwise be available to produce steam.

Boiler efficiency is the ratio of heat output (steam and
losses) to the heat input (fuel, feedwater, combustion
air). Flue-gas analysis and stack-temperature measurements can be used to monitor efficiency.

The percentage of excess combustion-air is determined
by analyzing the boiler exit gases for oxygen or carbon
dioxide (or both). Assuming that the gases consist solely
of O_2, CO_2 and N_2, the following equation can be used:

$$A_x = \frac{\%O_2}{0.266(100 - \%O_2 - \%CO_2) - \%O_2} \times 100$$

where $\%O_2$ and $\%CO_2$ are found by an Orsat-type
device [2].

Equations have been developed using just $\%O_2$, e.g.:

$$A_x = \frac{a \times \%O_2}{1 - 0.0476 \times \%O_2}$$

where Factor a is characteristic of the fuel being burned
[3]. Based on curves presented in Ref. 4:

a, natural gas $= 4.5557 - (0.026942 \times \%O_2)$
a, No. 2 fuel oil $= 4.43562 + (0.010208 \times \%O_2)$

Boiler efficiency and net flue-gas temperature* follow
a linear relationship:

$$E = 1/m \times (T - b)$$

where slope $1/m$ and intercept b/m vary with the type of
fuel and the percentage of excess air. The following
equations for finding m and b are based on curves
presented in Ref. 4:

Natural gas: $\log(-m) = -0.0025767A_x + 1.66403$
$\log(b) = -0.0025225A_x + 3.6226$

No. 2 fuel oil: $\log(-m) = -0.0027746A_x + 1.66792$
$\log(b) = -0.0027073A_x + 3.6432$

The calculation procedure becomes:

1. Determine flue-gas analysis of O_2 or CO_2, or both.
2. Determine the net stack exit temperature, T.
3. Calculate the percentage of excess air, A_x.
4. Calculate m and b.
5. Calculate boiler efficiency, E.

The calculated efficiency does not account for radiation or carbon losses. It is a measure of stack heat losses.

Once the efficiency is found, steam costs can be determined by the equation:

$$C_s = \frac{1,000 \times C_f \times H}{E}$$

This cost accounts only for the fuel portion. For a more
accurate figure one must include chemical treatment
costs, electric costs, labor costs, etc.

Efficiency calculations provide a sound basis for
evaluating conservation projects such as installation of
economizers and excess-air controls. Potential dollar
savings can be based on either constant steam outputs
or present fuel costs, as seen in Fig. 1 and 2.

Similarly, efficiency improvements at constant fuel
input will result in capacity increases, as shown in
Fig. 3.

A computer program was written to perform the
described calculations, using a Texas Instruments TI-59
programmable pocket calculator. The calculator eliminates the need for charts, tables and nomographs, while
providing the user with fast, dependable results. The

---

*Net flue-gas temperature is the difference between ambient temperature
and the stack temperature measured after the last heat-transfer surface of the
boiler.

Originally published July 16, 1979

Program for TI-59 calculator determines boiler efficiency and percentage of excess air. Inputs required are flue-gas temperature

Table I continues

Step	Key	Code	Step	Key	Code	Step	Key	Code	Step	Key	Code	Step	Key	Code	Step	Key	Code
000	76	LBL [1]	062	42	STO	124	04	4	186	00	0	248	02	2	310	06	6
001	11	A	063	15	15	125	02	2	187	00	0	249	02	2	311	02	2
002	42	STO	064	00	0	126	07	7	188	00	0	250	01	1	312	02	2
003	00	00	065	91	R/S	127	01	1	189	00	0	251	03	3	313	06	6
004	91	R/S	066	76	LBL [6]	128	07	7	190	00	0	252	69	OP	314	95	=
005	76	LBL [2]	067	17	B'	129	69	OP	191	69	OP	253	02	02	315	22	INV
006	12	B	068	22	INV	130	01	01	192	02	02	254	03	3	316	28	LOG
007	42	STO	069	86	STF	131	03	3	193	69	OP	255	06	6	317	42	STO
008	02	02	070	00	00	132	05	5	194	05	05	256	00	0	318	08	08
009	91	R/S	071	02	2	133	06	6	195	25	CLR [10]	257	00	0	319	76	LBL [14]
010	76	LBL [3]	072	02	2	134	02	2	196	69	OP	258	00	0	320	30	TAN
011	14	D	073	08	8	135	00	0	197	00	00	259	00	0	321	94	+/-
012	42	STO	074	08	8	136	00	0	198	53	(	260	00	0	322	85	+
013	03	03	075	02	2	137	00	0	199	43	RCL	261	00	0	323	43	RCL
014	91	R/S	076	42	STO	138	00	0	200	11	11	262	00	0	324	02	02
015	76	LBL [4]	077	05	05	139	00	0	201	65	×	263	00	0	325	95	=
016	19	D'	078	93	.	140	00	0	202	43	RCL	264	69	OP	326	55	÷
017	42	STO	079	00	0	141	69	OP	203	00	00	265	03	03	327	43	RCL
018	01	01	080	02	2	142	02	02	204	85	+	266	69	OP	328	07	07
019	91	R/S	081	06	6	143	69	OP	205	43	RCL	267	05	05	329	95	=
020	76	LBL [5]	082	09	9	144	05	05	206	12	12	268	98	ADV [12]	330	42	STO
021	16	A'	083	04	4	145	25	CLR [8]	207	54	)	269	93	.	331	09	09
022	86	STF	084	02	2	146	69	OP	208	65	×	270	00	0	332	06	6 [15]
023	00	00	085	94	+/-	147	00	00	209	43	RCL	271	00	0	333	01	1
024	01	1	086	42	STO	148	01	1	210	00	00	272	02	2	334	00	0
025	09	9	087	11	11	149	06	6	211	55	÷	273	05	5	335	00	0
026	04	4	088	04	4	150	01	1	212	53	(	274	07	7	336	03	3
027	05	5	089	93	.	151	03	3	213	01	1	275	06	6	337	02	2
028	08	8	090	05	5	152	03	3	214	75	-	276	07	7	338	00	0
029	42	STO	091	05	5	153	07	7	215	93	.	277	94	+/-	339	03	3
030	05	05	092	05	5	154	69	OP	216	00	0	278	65	×	340	69	OP
031	93	.	093	07	7	155	01	01	217	04	4	279	43	RCL	341	04	04
032	00	0	094	42	STO	156	01	1	218	07	7	280	06	06	342	43	RCL
033	01	1	095	12	12	157	07	7	219	06	6	281	85	+	343	00	00
034	00	0	096	93	.	158	06	6	220	65	×	282	01	1	344	69	OP [16]
035	02	2	097	01	1	159	02	2	221	43	RCL	283	93	.	345	06	06
036	00	0	098	07	7	160	00	0	222	00	00	284	06	6	346	03	3
037	08	8	099	42	STO	161	00	0	223	54	)	285	06	6	347	07	7
038	42	STO	100	13	13	162	00	0	224	95	=	286	04	4	348	05	5
039	11	11	101	01	1	163	00	0	225	42	STO [11]	287	00	0	349	07	7
040	04	4	102	93	.	164	00	0	226	06	06	288	03	3	350	06	6
041	93	.	103	09	9	165	00	0	227	66	PAU	289	95	=	351	05	5
042	04	4	104	42	STO	166	69	OP	228	66	PAU	290	22	INV	352	02	2
043	03	3	105	14	14	167	02	02	229	66	PAU	291	28	LOG	353	01	1
044	05	5	106	01	1	168	69	OP	230	87	IFF	292	94	+/-	354	69	OP
045	06	6	107	05	5	169	05	05	231	00	00	293	42	STO	355	04	04
046	02	2	108	93	.	170	25	CLR [9]	232	39	COS	294	07	07	356	43	RCL
047	42	STO	109	05	5	171	69	OP	233	68	NOP	295	93	. [13]	357	02	02
048	12	12	110	42	STO	172	00	00	234	02	2	296	00	0	358	69	OP [17]
049	93	.	111	15	15	173	02	2	235	01	1	297	00	0	359	06	06
050	01	1	112	00	0	174	07	7	236	04	4	298	02	2	360	06	6
051	05	5	113	91	R/S	175	03	3	237	01	1	299	05	5	361	01	1
052	42	STO	114	76	LBL [7]	176	02	2	238	01	1	300	02	2	362	00	0
053	13	13	115	15	E	177	01	1	239	07	7	301	02	2	363	00	0
054	93	.	116	25	CLR	178	03	3	240	69	OP	302	05	5	364	04	4
055	08	8	117	69	OP	179	69	OP	241	01	01	303	94	+/-	365	04	4
056	42	STO	118	00	00	180	01	01	242	02	2	304	65	×	366	03	3
057	14	14	119	01	1	181	01	1	243	07	7	305	43	RCL	367	06	6
058	01	1	120	04	4	182	06	6	244	06	6	306	06	06	368	69	OP
059	04	4	121	03	3	183	06	6	245	02	2	307	85	+	369	04	04
060	93	.	122	02	2	184	02	2	246	00	0	308	03	3	370	43	RCL
061	02	2	123	02	2	185	00	0	247	00	0	309	93	.	371	06	06

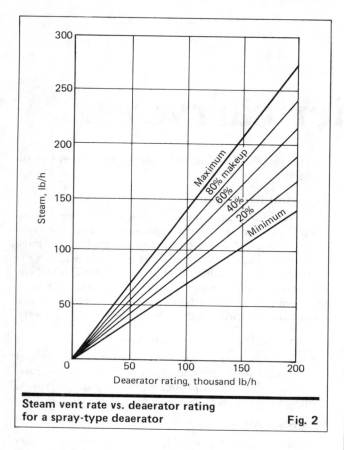

Steam vent rate vs. deaerator rating for a spray-type deaerator   **Fig. 2**

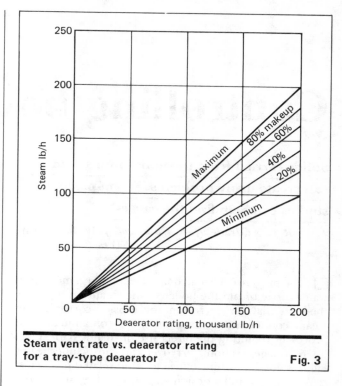

Steam vent rate vs. deaerator rating for a tray-type deaerator   **Fig. 3**

pH from about 7.8 to 7.0. Trays in the deaerator will remove the free CO_2.

Neutralizing amines can be injected into the boiler feedwater, ahead of the boiler. These amines, which include cyclohexylamine, benzylamine and morpholine, volatilize in the boiler and, upon condensation, neutralize the carbonic acid, raising the pH above 7.0 to 8.0 or 8.3. These chemicals are added in direct proportion to the amount of free carbon dioxide present or generated in the boiler. Insufficient steam stripping in the deaerator to remove free CO_2 results in extra use of amines.

Deaerator vent steam—average cases

In practice, deaerator vent-steam rates range from 0.05 to 0.14% of the deaerator rating. The actual amount is dependent on: the type of deaerator (which determines efficiency of gas removal); amount of makeup water; properties of makeup water; and condition of condensate return.

To estimate the amount of steam venting from spray- and tray-type deaerators (the two most common types), Figs. 2 and 3 illustrate the amounts for deaerators rated up to 200,000 lb/h. In the case of a 100,000-lb/h unit of the spray type, the steam vent rate varies from a minimum of 70 to a maximum of 140 lb/h. For a tray type of the same size, the rate ranges from 50 to 100 lb/h.

Energy losses

Steam venting from deaerating heaters represents a significant heat loss. It may range from a high of 0.8% down to 0.3% of the energy in the heated feedwater.

Until recently, there has been no practical means of recovering energy in the vent steam. Industry has not accepted the shell-and-tube heat exchanger for deaerator vent condensing because its configuration, size, weight, and thermal and hydraulic characteristics are not compatible with the deaerator heat and water balance. However, a new type of heat exchanger has become available for recovering energy from the deaerator vent steam, by using it to preheat makeup water [9].

References

1. Korten, E. C., The ASME Boiler and Pressure Code, *TAPPI*, Vol. 37, No. 6, June 1954, p. 242.
2. Othmer, D. F., *Ind. Eng. Chem.*, Vol. 26, p. 576 (1929).
3. Reid, William T., "External Corrosion and Deposits in Boilers and Gas Turbines," Elsevier Pub. Co., Amsterdam, 1971.
4. "Betz Handbook of Industrial Water Conditioning," 7th ed., Betz Laboratories, Inc., Trevose, Pa., 1976.
5. Obrecht, Malvern R., Steam and Condensate Return Line Corrosion: Its Causes and Cures, *Heat./Piping/Air Cond.*, July 1964, p. 117.
6. Tresden, R. S., Guarding Against Hydrogen Embrittlement, *Chem. Eng.*, June 29, 1981, p. 105.
7. Monroe, E. S., Jr., Effects of CO_2 in Steam Systems, *Chem. Eng.*, Mar. 23, 1981, p. 209.
8. Monroe, E. S., Jr., Condensate Recovery Systems, *Chem. Eng.*, June 13, 1983, p. 119, Fig. 6.
9. HELEX Div. of A. C. Knox, Inc., Cincinnati, Ohio.

The author

Arthur C. Knox is the principal of A. C. Knox, Inc., Consulting Engineers, 525 Purcel Ave., P.O. Box 5029, Cincinnati, OH 45205; phone: (513) 921-5028. A graduate of the University of Cincinnati, he is is a licensed professional engineer in a number of states. He has 25 years of experience in industrial utilities and energy systems, holds patents on heat exchangers, and has authored articles on pollution control, fuels and combustion.

Controlling boiler carryover

Solids carried from the boiler into steam can create many problems. Steam-purity studies can help find the causes.

R. C. Andrade, J. A. Gates and *J. W. McCarthy,*
Drew Chemical Corp.

□ The presence of small quantities of inorganic salts in water carried from the boiler to the steam can increase the potential for corrosion (or erosion-corrosion) in steam condensate systems or cause contamination in processes requiring the direct use of steam. With steam for power generation, carryover can cause superheater failures, loss of turbine efficiency, and related problems.

With a carefully designed steam-purity study, the causes of carryover can be pinpointed, then eliminated.

Causes of carryover

Carryover into the steam of substances present in boiler water is caused both by entrainment of small droplets of boiler water in the steam leaving the drum and by volatilization of salts that are dissolved in the steam. Mechanical entrainment, which can occur in all steam generators, can be minimized through mechanical or operational changes, so this type of carryover is the most common target of steam-purity studies. (Volatile carryover, while of major concern in high-pressure installations, cannot be prevented by mechanical or operational modifications, and will not be discussed further.)

Mechanical entrainment can be divided into three categories: priming, foaming, and equipment failure.

Priming

Priming usually results from a sudden reduction in boiler pressure caused by a rapid increase in the steam load. This causes steam bubbles to form throughout the mass of water in the steam drum, flooding the separators or dry pipe. Priming may also result from excessively high water levels. Priming results in a violent "throwing" of large slugs of boiler water into the steam. The problem can usually be minimized by changes in operation.

Foaming

Foaming is the buildup of bubbles on the water surface in the steam drum. This reduces the steam release space, and, by various mechanisms, causes mechanical entrainment. Foaming is almost always the result of improper chemical conditions in the boiler water, including alkalinity, suspended solids, dissolved solids, and organic surfactants and detergents. Your water-treatment-chemical supplier should provide a program to control the chemistry of the boiler water, thereby regulating these conditions.

Equipment failure

Boiler drums may contain baffles, screens, mesh mist-eliminators and centrifugal separators to improve separation of water droplets from steam. Each element must be kept tight and clean. A quarter-inch gap between the sections of cover baffles over the generating tubes can allow sufficient water to bypass the separators to negate their operation. Similarly, deposits on screens or mist-eliminators can prevent them from functioning properly.

Steam-purity measurement

Conducting a steam-purity study involves the proper collection of steam samples, their accurate analysis, and the establishment of proper operating conditions to achieve meaningful results.

Sample collection

Accurate sampling is difficult. The very fine water droplets in saturated steam remain dispersed uniformly for only several tube diameters in the direction of flow; then they agglomerate and run along the tube walls.

Sampling superheated steam is even more difficult. Particulate matter and substances soluble in the steam can deposit on the sampling-line walls, effectively depleting the sample of some important components.

The basis of the problem is that a two-phase, and sometimes a three-phase, vapor—liquid—solid dynamic system must be sampled to reflect the absolute composition of the total mass. The special sampling nozzle designs specified by ASTM and ASME are recommended. However, installation of such nozzles generally requires that the boiler be shut down first.

Often, a carryover problem occurs suddenly while the boiler is being operated at high capacity, when a shutdown is impossible. The plant's engineers may then opt to use a standard steam takeoff. Such samples should be taken from a point as close as possible to the boiler, and the results interpreted for their relative values only.

Sample analysis

The following methods have been used for the online analysis of steam samples:
- Ion exchange.
- Conductivity.
- Flame photometry.
- Specific-ion electrodes.
- Radioactive tracers.

Of these, the specific-ion electrode method for measuring the sodium content of the steam is considered to offer the most benefits. This method relies on the ratio

Originally published December 26, 1983

of sodium to dissolved solids being the same in the steam as in the boiler water from which it came. From experience, we know that the solids-to-sodium ratio is usually in the range of 2.8—3.0 to one. Furthermore, the sodium content in the saturated steam can be directly related to the potential for deposit formation in both turbines and superheaters (Table I).

The specific-ion electrode offers high sensitivity (0.1 ppb Na) and low lag time. The lag time that does occur may tend to shave off the highest peaks, but still clearly shows meaningful deviations. The unit is portable, and easy to operate and maintain.

Conducting the tests

A sufficient amount of baseline data is necessary to evaluate a potential carryover situation. This usually involves the collection and analysis of steam samples at various loads, with the boiler in a base-loaded (no load swings) condition.

With the base line established, samples should be collected and analyzed with the boiler operating under normal loading conditions. It is important that boiler-water chemical conditions be kept within their recommended limits during this phase of testing. Since most sodium analyzers incorporate continuous strip-chart re-

corders, data can easily be collected for 12 to 24 hours (or longer). These data can then be compared with the baseline study to determine any variations.

If the problem cannot be resolved during these initial tests, alternative conditions must be established at different boiler loads, such as:

■ High and low water levels in the steam drum.
■ Rapid load swings (usually accomplished with the boiler on manual control).
■ Overconcentration of the boiler water (excessive conductivity).

Parameters should be varied individually, and detailed records kept. In addition to records of data pertinent to the above variables, such items as a fuel change, gas pressure drop, feedwater temperature change, change in condensate-return flow or source, etc., should be included. Reference samples of the boiler water should be taken at a number of points during the test, especially before and after any change that would have a significant effect on boiler-water chemistry.

Implementing these procedures will assure the most accurate test results possible. Additionally, they will enable keeping a close watch on steam purity and avoiding the downtime and lost efficiency caused by carryover.

The following are examples of the use of steam studies to determine the basic causes of carryover.

Study in 300-psig refinery boilers

In a Southwestern refinery, the boilers had been in a clean condition for several years, except that the superheaters required acid cleaning at each annual inspection. Steam-purity studies had never been carried out to determine the cause of carryover.

Sample points were determined and stainless-steel sample tubing and coolers were installed at ground level. Although the control-board reading indicated a 50%

Relation of sodium levels to boiler deposition			Table I
Sodium, ppb	Total solids, ppm	Turbine deposition	Superheater deposition
3.3	0.01	No	No
3.3-33	0.01-0.1	Possible	No
33-333	0.1-1.0	Yes	Possible
333	1.0	Yes	Yes

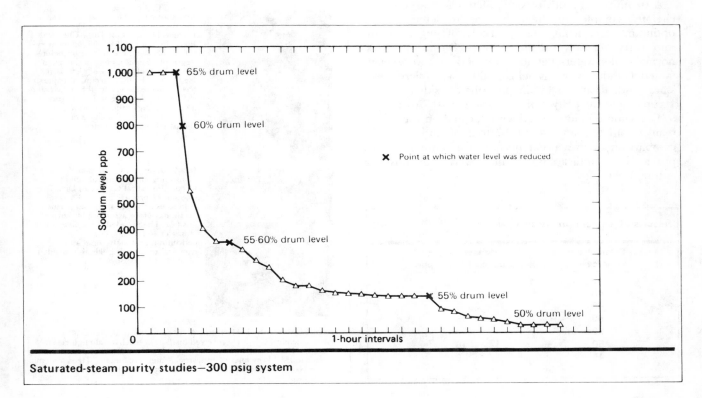

Saturated-steam purity studies—300 psig system

water level in the steam drum, the onsite gage reading varied from 60 to 80%. The high water-level was suspected of contributing to the carryover problem.

To help control carryover, the boiler-water total alkalinity had been controlled within the recommended range of 450 to 650 ppm (but generally at 450 ppm) by adjusting the blowdown rate. Despite alkalinity control, deposition was occurring in the superheater sections.

The sample line was heavily purged in preparation for the steam-purity test, the sodium analyzer was calibrated, and operation was stabilized. Measured sodium levels quickly pegged out at 1,000 ppb. Testing was continued for several hours without any reduction in sodium level. (The initial tests were performed without any change in plant operations.)

The second phase of testing involved step reductions from the initial observed steam-drum level of 65% down to 50% in 5% decrements, with sodium levels being monitored after operations stabilized at each drum level. The plotted data (p. 52) show the dramatic reduction of sodium from a concentration of 1,000 ppb to 30 ppb.

Since the only operating variable that had been changed was the steam-drum water level, this factor was considered responsible for the high sodium level in the saturated steam. By maintaining the level at 50% the carryover problem had been solved.

The boiler-plant operator and instrument technician worked together to calibrate the instrument-board level meters. Later, it was found that the blowdown rate could be decreased somewhat to maintain the total alkalinity at the upper end of the recommended range without increasing impurity carryover in the saturated steam. A subsequent boiler inspection confirmed the absence of deposition in the superheaters.

Study of petrochemical complex's boilers

A steam-purity study was conducted at a large petrochemical complex on the Gulf Coast to determine the optimum steam-drum water-level control range, to minimize carryover to the steam turbines. During the tests, normal boiler-water-chemical control ranges were maintained. Conductivity was held at 160 to 170 micromhos, silica residuals at 2 to 3 ppm, phosphate residuals at 8 to 10 ppm, and the pH within the range of 10.7 to 11.0.

The sample points tested were located on top of the main steam line and at the bottom of this line. The comparison of measurements taken at both locations provided an indication of the severity of possible entrainment.

During the initial tests, the water level was held at 42%, with a constant steam rate of 140,000 lb/h. The sample obtained from the top of the line had a sodium level of 0.6 ppb, whereas the one from the bottom had a level of 4.0 ppb.

As testing continued, the boiler feedwater pumps were switched; causing a momentary change in the system's hydraulic stability. The feedwater rate to the boiler sustained a sudden drop, followed by a large upward surge. As a result, the water level rose from 40 to 48%, with an increase in the sodium reading to 110 ppb.

Operating conditions were again stabilized at a water level of 42%, with a corresponding sodium concentration of 4.0 ppb. The water level was then slowly increased and stabilized at each level. These adjustments were made over a period of several hours to ensure that the sodium analyzer was recording a constant sodium concentration at each water level. The results are summarized in Table II.

After completing these tests, we recommended that the steam-drum water level be held within the range of 42 to 48%, with a target level of 45%. This mode of operation would minimize carryover, while avoiding the annoyance of frequent low-water-level alarms. During the tests, is was noted that the control-board level readings and the actual drum's gage-glass level corresponded within plus or minus 0.5 to 1%.

This steam-purity study enabled us to identify two critical operational factors for limiting carryover. Potential problems have been avoided by maintaining the water level below 48%, and by minimizing the occurrence of sudden water-level surges.

Results of a steam-purity test   Table II

Steam-drum water level, %	Steam sodium concentration, ppb
42	4
45	4
48	4
50	15
52	30
50	18
45	6

The authors

Ronald C. Andrade is Manager, Consulting and Technical Services, Industrial Chemicals Div., Drew Chemical Corp., One Drew Chemical Plaza, Boonton, NJ 07005, telephone: (201) 263-7600. He holds a bachelor's degree in chemical engineering from the College of the City of New York. He has written many technical papers, has conducted seminars throughout the U.S., South America and Europe, and is a contributing author to Drew Chemical's text, "Principles of Industrial Water Treatment."

Jay A. Gates is a Consultant, Consulting and Technical Services Group, Industrial Chemicals Div., Drew Chemical Corp. He has held several field-sales and field-sales-management positions before assuming his current position. He attended the University of Houston and Texas A&M, concentrating in petroleum and chemical engineering. He is a member of the Gas Processors Assn.

John W. McCarthy is Marketing Manager, Industrial Chemicals Div., Drew Chemical Corp. He received his B.S. in mechanical engineering from the New Jersey Institute of Technology, and is a major contributing author to the "Principles of Industrial Water Treatment." He is a member of the National Assn. of Corrosion Engineers and the American Soc. of Mechanical Engineers.

Section II
Cooling

Cost parameters for surface-condensing refrigeration systems

Fig. 3 and 4 curve number	Capacity range, 1,000 gal/d	Parameter a	b
1	375-1,000	11,000	0.187
2	750-1,500	9,620	0.187
3	150-400	7,990	0.208
4	300-800	6,920	0.208
5	1,250-2,000	2,310	0.322
6	2,500-4,000	1,850	0.322
7	750-1,000	8,540	0.215
8	1,500-2,000	7,360	0.215

influencing costs are the mode of operation—continuous or intermittent—and certain design conditions, such as whether the system includes a chiller precooler for dehumidifying the gas stream.

Costs in May 1982 dollars of intermittently operated surface-condensing systems—those that must be shut down for one hour daily for defrosting—are plotted in Fig. 3. Here, Curves 1 and 2 cover systems that include chiller precoolers, and Curves 3 and 4 those that do not. Additionally, Curves 1 and 3 and Curves 2 and 4 correspond, respectively, to outlet volatile-vapor concentrations of 0.33 and 0.67 lb/1,000 gal of liquid transferred from the source [4].

(Note: one gallon of transferred liquid displaces one gallon of vapor and air mixture; for gasoline vapors at 70°F and 1 atm, these are, respectively, equivalent to 1.45% and 2.9% by volume.)

Costs of continuously operated surface-condensing systems are plotted in Fig. 4.

Curves 7 and 8 and Points C and D give costs of systems of one set of compressors, each set with a split condensing coil (while one part of the coil is condensing, the other is defrosting). Curves 5 and 6 and Points A and B provide costs of systems of two sets of compressors, each set having dual, full-capacity coils.

Curves 5 and 7 and Points A and C correspond to an outlet volatile-vapor concentration of 0.33 lb/1,000 gal

of transferred liquid; and Curves 6 and 8 and Points B and D to 0.67 lb/1,000. Additionally, Points A through D represent costs of systems without precoolers.

Each system comes with a volatile-vapor analyzer, condenser chart recorder, and recovered-product meter.

The systems with precoolers do not include the cost of the heat-transfer fluid (usually ethylene glycol). The quantity of fluid required varies with system capacity; a typical system needs 150 lb. This would add only about $50 to the purchased cost of the equipment, based on May 1982 prices [5].

Costs of surface-condensing systems can be approximated via Eq. (4):

$$C_s = aG^b \qquad (4)$$

Here, C_s = purchase cost in May 1982 dollars, and a, b = parameters. Values for a and b are listed in the table.

Costs of direct-condensing systems

Fig. 5 displays costs of direct-contact condensing systems in terms of equipment size in tonnage. Eq. (5) fits the data in Fig. 5:

$$C_d = 8.12 + 5.69T \qquad (5)$$

Here, C_d = purchase cost of contact-condensing system in November 1979 dollars, and T = cooling capacity in tons of refrigeration.

Operating costs

Refrigeration systems require little operating or maintenance labor—usually about 1/2 labor-hours/shift for each [6]. However, electricity costs (for running compressors, circulation pumps, etc.) can be significant. In the case of the surface-condensing system, average electricity usage ranges from 4.1–4.3 kWh/1,000 gal of inlet flow, with 4.15 kWh being typical [4]. That of the contact-condensing system is less, approximately 2 kW/ton in the range 35–40°F [1].

The value of the vapor condensate recovered should be subtracted from the operating and maintenance costs and capital charges. In some instances, this recovery credit could exceed these costs. To compute the annual credit, multiply the condensate mass, m_c, by the value of the condensate and the number of hours that the system operates annually.

Acknowledgment

The authors are grateful to Robert J. Honegger of GATX Terminals Corp., who provided valuable material for this article.

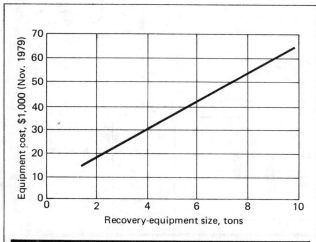

Purchase costs of direct-contact-condensing refrigeration systems [1]   **Fig. 5**

References

1. Honegger, R. J., "Environmental Control Systems: Refrigeration Methods of Vapor Recovery," Gard, Inc., Niles, Ill., Dec. 21, 1979.
2. Smith, J. M., and Van Ness, H. C., "Introduction to Chemical Engineering Thermodynamics," 2nd ed., McGraw-Hill, Inc., New York, 1959.
3. Mehra, Y. R., Refrigeration Systems for Low-Temperature Processes, *Chem. Eng.*, July 12, 1982, p. 94.
4. Price data from Edwards Engineering Corp., Pompton Plains, N.J., 1982.
5. *Chemical Marketing Reporter*, May 17, 1982, p. 56.
6. Vatavuk, W. M., and Neveril, R. B, Estimating Costs of Air-Pollution Control Systems, Part II: Factors for Estimating Capital and Operating Costs, *Chem. Eng.*, Nov. 3, 1980, p. 157.

Trouble-shooting compression refrigeration systems

Comparing operating conditions to design values quickly locates the source of problems that can arise in refrigeration systems. Here are procedures for performing such analyses and the corrective actions to be taken.

Kenneth J. Vargas, Gulf Canada Resources Inc.

☐ An efficient way to troubleshoot a compression refrigeration system is by using a pressure-enthalpy chart for the refrigerant in the system [1,3].

The design conditions for the refrigeration system being studied can be superimposed on the operating conditions on such a chart. Thus, we can compare the operating cycle to the design values.

We will consider here the smaller refrigeration systems (up to 20 hp) and the larger units. The reason for this division is that some problems such as an undercharge or overcharge of refrigerant in the system, while common to the smaller systems, are not often encountered in the larger ones.

Small refrigeration systems

The most effective method for detecting faults in the smaller units is to determine the suction and discharge pressures at the compressor. Knowing the pressure, we

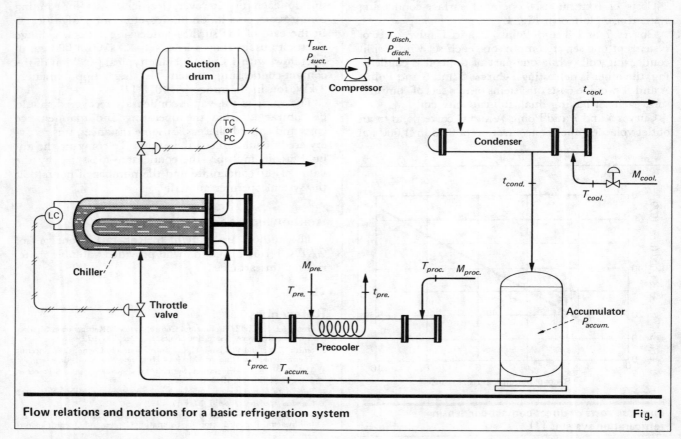

Flow relations and notations for a basic refrigeration system

Fig. 1

Originally published March 22, 1982

can find the temperature automatically from the refrigerant charts [1,3].

Usually, these smaller units have provisions for hooking up service equipment such as valves and gages in order to add refrigerant. These service points are located before and after the compressor.

Some of the most common problems, their causes and remedies for smaller refrigeration units are listed in Table I. It is probably best to construct a pressure-enthalpy chart for the operating conditions, and compare these with the design values. Then, by using Table I, we can determine the problems. Care must be taken with the smaller units to avoid an overcharge or undercharge of refrigerant.

Large refrigeration systems

In order to simplify the analysis of a refrigeration system for troubleshooting, we will use the notation shown in Fig. 1. Thus, when we refer to a pressure, temperature or flow, we will use its symbol. Subcoolers, economizers, etc. will be neglected in order to clarify the troubleshooting procedures—we will consider only a basic refrigeration system (Fig. 1).

The first step in troubleshooting large systems is to draw a pressure-enthalpy diagram of the operating conditions. A comparison of the data in this diagram to the design conditions will give the clues to the problems. These problems can be categorized as:

- Fouling of precooler.
- Impurities in the refrigerant.
- Fouling of the chiller.
- Malfunctions of the throttling valves.
- Fouling or loss of capacity of the condenser.
- Malfunctions of the compressor.

We will examine each of these problems and analyze their respective symptoms.

Fouling of precooler

If the precooler becomes fouled, the chiller will not be able to cool the process fluid, $M_{Proc.}$, to the desired temperature. This fouling could occur on the side of the process fluid or of the cooling-medium fluid, $M_{Pre.}$.

From the heat-exchanger design sheets, we obtain the duty, q, and the inlet and outlet temperatures for both the shellside and tubeside of the exchanger. We can now calculate the heat-transfer coefficient, U, from:

$$q = UA\,[f(LMTD)] \qquad (1)$$

where q = duty, Btu/h; A = heat-exchanger (i.e., tube bundle) surface area, ft²; U = heat-transfer coefficient, Btu/(h)(ft²)(°F); f = heat-exchanger correction factor, dimensionless (this factor depends on heat-exchanger characteristics). For countercurrent flow $f = 1.0$; $(LMTD)$ = log mean temperature difference, °F.

The log mean temperature difference is the approach of the ΔTs between the shellside and tubeside. For countercurrent flow (as shown by the sketch) we calculate U from:

$$(LMTD) = \frac{(T_{hot} - t_{cold}) - (T_{cold} - t_{hot})}{\ln\left(\dfrac{T_{hot} - t_{cold}}{T_{cold} - t_{hot}}\right)} \qquad (2)$$

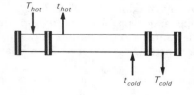

Trouble-shooting small refrigeration units	Table I

Symptom: High discharge pressure	
Cause	**Remedy**
Ambient conditions too hot for air or water.	Change location of unit to obtain cooler air or water for condenser.
Insufficient air across condenser.	Check for obstructions on condenser coils or faulty fan operation.
Refrigeration overcharge.	Purge.
Air in refrigerant system. This gives an extreme increase in head pressure.	Purge air at highest point of condensing unit (air is lighter than refrigerant).
Fouled condenser.	Clean or replace condenser.
No water.	Open condenser water valve.

Symptom: Low discharge pressure	
Cause	**Remedy**
Shortage of refrigerant.	Find and fix leak. Recharge refrigerant reservoir.
Malfunction of compressor's suction or discharge valves.	Clean or replace valves or seats. Overhaul compressor.

Symptom: Low suction pressure	
Cause	**Remedy**
Insufficient process fluid in the chiller.	Check superheat at chiller outlet. Increase the flow of process fluid to chiller by eliminating obstructions, etc.
Poor refrigerant flow.	Check for restrictions in refrigerant flow in line or at expansion valve. Clean out line or expansion valve.
Short refrigerant charge.	Find refrigerant leak (characterized by hissing at expansion valve because high-pressure vapor rather than liquid passes through valve to evaporator). Refill.
Low process temperature	No problem (low head pressure will be observed as well).

Symptom: High suction pressure	
Cause	**Remedy**
High loading of evaporator coil.	Too hot a load for refrigerant capacity. Upgrade unit.
System operates at low superheat.	Expansion valve has to be adjusted or compressor damage may occur.

Symptom: Process side of chiller temperature too high	
Cause	**Remedy**
Refrigerant shortage	Fix leak. Refill with refrigerant.
Expansion valve plugged, or restriction at refrigerant suction.	Change or repair valve or line.
Misadjustment of expansion valve.	Lower superheat setting for expansion valve.
Unit too small.	Debottleneck and upgrade refrigeration capacity.
Fouled chiller.	Clean.

Note: For an exchanger where there is a change of state and a temperature change, the (LMTD) is an average for each state.

After calculating the appropriate numerical values, we determine U from:

$$U = q/Af(LMTD) \qquad (3)$$

By comparing the value of U for the operating unit as calculated from Eq. (3) to the design value for U, fouling can be detected. The ratio of the calculated value of U to the design value of U should be in the range of 0.90 to 1.00. If this is not the case, fouling is the most probable cause. A problem similar to fouling is the drop in velocity of the fluid through the tubeside.

The first thing to do to defoul a heat exchanger is to determine whether the tubeside or shellside is fouled. In any service, one side of the exchanger is more prone to fouling than the other. The side that is suspect should be cleaned first. If the U value does not significantly improve after the exchanger is put back into operation, the other side should also be cleaned.

We will cover fouling and loss of fluid velocities in greater detail when we review fouling of the chiller. This will give us a better appreciation of the actual conditions causing decreases in the values of the overall heat-transfer coefficient, U.

Impurities in the refrigerant

On occasion, it may be desirable to change the physical properties of a refrigerant by adding lighter- or heavier-molecular-weight components to an existing refrigerant. The incremental returns, however, from such a procedure are slight compared to the problems that may arise.

An impure refrigerant undergoes changes in almost all of its pressure/temperature characteristics. Hence, the pressure-enthalpy charts have to be drawn for the specific composition of the refrigerant. Commonly, impurities in a refrigerant disrupt the refrigeration cycle. Substances such as air in fluorinated-hydrocarbon refrigerant or ethane in propane can significantly affect the shape of the enthalpy curve of the refrigeration cycle.

The first thing to do is to plot a pressure-enthalpy diagram for the refrigeration system, as shown in Fig. 2* by the solid lines. Label each line in the cycle. To define the cycle, we need the suction pressure and temperature, $P_{suct.}$ and $T_{suct.}$, respectively; discharge pressure and temperature, $P_{disch.}$ and $T_{disch.}$; condenser temperature, $t_{cond.}$; and accumulator pressure, $P_{accum.}$.

Let us next consider the situation where impurities are present in the refrigerant. The refrigeration cycle is now defined by the following:

$T_{suct.} = 40°F$, $T_{disch.} = 180°F$, $t_{cond.} = 90°F$

$P_{suct.} = 40$ psia, $P_{disch.} = 300$ psia, $P_{accum.} = 250$ psia

The plot for the cycle containing an impure refrigerant is shown by the dotted lines in Fig. 2.

One of the major problems with impurities in the refrigerant is damage to the compressor. This may arise if the suction pressure is reduced by a change in the

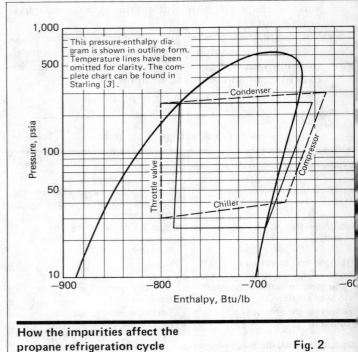

How the impurities affect the propane refrigeration cycle   **Fig. 2**

refrigerant composition or by impurities containing water. Water forms ice and hydrates[†] and has other unwanted side effects in hydrocarbon refrigerants.

It is better to operate the refrigeration unit at design conditions, and not get into unpleasant situations later on. If we observe a cycle such as that shown by the dotted lines in Fig. 2, it may not necessarily point to refrigerant impurities. The following items should be checked:

■ Pressure/temperature gages on compressor suction and discharge.
■ Chiller level is within range.
■ Condenser/accumulator has an adequate amount of liquid in it, as indicated by level.

To confirm the presence of impurities in the refrigerant, we take a sample of the refrigerant, or purge the system of lighter substances at the top of the condenser/accumulator.

Chiller fouling

Chiller fouling is indicated in refrigeration systems when process chilling is lost with little or no change in the temperature and pressure conditions at the compressor suction or discharge. As before, compare the pressure/enthalpy chart with the design values. If no significant change in the overall cycle is evident and loss of refrigeration capacity is present, the problem is in the chiller.

All problems with chiller capacity manifest themselves with a decrease in the heat-transfer coefficient, U. As with any heat exchanger, Eq. (1) will model the situation. A decrease in U can be due to several factors. The most common is fouling. Loss in U can also arise from a loss in fluid velocity on the process side of the chiller or

---

*The pressure-enthalpy diagram of Fig. 2 is shown in outline form. The detailed pressure-enthalpy chart for propane is given by Starling [3].

[†]Hydrates are hydrocarbon-and-water mixtures that freeze at fairly high temperatures.

from level-control problems. First, let us consider fouling in the chiller:

Fouling—As the chiller becomes fouled, U decreases as does the heat duty q. However, these are not proportional, and U is usually more pronounced—the $(LMTD)$ restores equilibrium by increasing. Consider the conditions shown in Fig. 3 for a chiller; compare the nonfouled and fouled cases to enable us to understand what is happening.

Nonfouled chiller—Apply Eq. (1) and let $f = 1.0$ and consider that the heat-transfer area, A, remains fixed. Then:

$$U = q/A(LMTD) \qquad (3)$$

Next, substitute into Eq. (2) to find:

$$(LMTD) = \frac{(30 - 0) - (10 - 0)}{\ln (30/10)} = \frac{20}{1.10} \simeq 18.2°F$$

Now, find the duty q. Care must be taken if there is a change of state in the chiller. The energy–mass balance around the chiller is:

$$q = M_{gas}H_{gas}^n + M_{liq.}H_{liq.}^n - [m_{gas}H_{gas}^{n'} + m_{liq.}^{n'}H_{liq.}^n.]$$

where M = mass flowrate in, lb/h; m = mass flowrate out, lb/h; H^n = enthalpy at $n°F$, Btu/lb.

To proceed with our example, let the hydrocarbon streams be:

Stream	lb/h	psia	Molecular weight
M_{gas}	10,000	1,000	20
$M_{liq.}$	0		
m_{gas}	8,000	1,000	17.55
$m_{liq.}$	2,000		30

From tables of enthalpies for hydrocarbon, we find:

$$H_{gas}^{30°} = 152 \text{ Btu/lb}$$
$$H_{gas}^{10°} = 150 \text{ Btu/lb}$$
$$H_{liq.}^{10°} = -35 \text{ Btu/lb}$$

We find the heat duty, q, to be:

$$q = 10,000(152) - [8,000(150) + 2,000(-35)]$$
$$q = 390,000 \text{ Btu/h}$$

By substituting the appropriate values into Eq. (3), calculate the overall heat-transfer coefficient in terms of the surface area, A, as:

$$U = \frac{390,000}{A(18.2)} \simeq \frac{21,429}{A} \text{ Btu/(h)(ft}^2)(°F)$$

Fouled chiller—We begin the analysis for this case by calculating the $(LMTD)$ for the fouled chiller:

$$(LMTD) = \frac{(30 - 0) - (20 - 0)}{\ln (30/20)} = 24.7°F$$

Because of poor heat transfer across the tubes due to fouling, less process gas will condense in the tubes. For illustrative purposes, let us assume that 1,500 lb/h condenses, vs. 2,000 lb/h for the nonfouled case. The heat duty for the fouled chiller becomes:

$$q = 10,000(152) - [8,500(155) + 1,500(-30)]$$
$$q = 247,500 \text{ Btu/h}$$

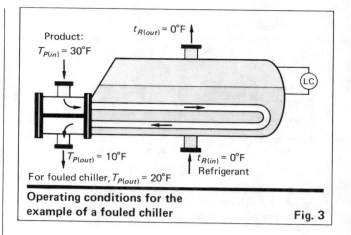

Operating conditions for the example of a fouled chiller   **Fig. 3**

The heat-transfer coefficient, U_F, for the fouled exchanger becomes:

$$U_F = 247,500/A(24.7) \simeq 10,020/A$$

Hence, the ratio $U_F/U = (10,020/A)/(21,429/A)$, or $U_F \simeq (1/2)U$.

To understand how fouling comes about, let us calculate U empirically from the following equation:

$$\frac{1}{U} = \frac{1}{h_o} + r_o + r_w + r_i\left(\frac{A_o}{A_i}\right) + \frac{1}{h_i}\left(\frac{A_o}{A_i}\right) \qquad (4)$$

where h_o and h_i are the outside and inside heat-transfer coefficients, respectively, Btu/(h)(ft^2)(°F); r_o and r_i are the outside and inside scale factors, and r_w is the transfer factor for the metal wall, (h)(ft^2)(°F)/Btu; and A_o and A_i are the outside and inside area of the tubes, ft^2.

The inside and outside heat-transfer coefficients, h_i and h_o, are a function of diameter, velocity, viscosity, specific heat, thermal conductivity and length. The variables for this relationship change according to whether the flow is laminar ($N_{Re} \leqslant 2,100$) or turbulent ($N_{Re} > 2,100$). Most chiller processes are designed for turbulent flow through the tubes because this results in better heat exchange.

Let us assume that fouling is on the process side (i.e., inside the tubes) and that the h_i and h_o do not change (only viscosity or velocity can change them). Assume also that for a clean chiller the following values apply:

$$h_o = 300 \text{ Btu/(h)(ft}^2)(°F)$$
$$h_i = 100 \text{ Btu/(h)(ft}^2)(°F)$$
$$r_w = \text{Negligible}$$
$$r_o = 0.0015 \text{ (h)(ft}^2)(°F)/Btu$$
$$r_i = 0.001 \text{ (h)(ft}^2)(°F)/Btu$$

We then substitute into Eq. (4), letting the value $A_o/A_i \simeq 1$, in order to evaluate U for the clean chiller:

$$\frac{1}{U} = \frac{1}{300} + 0.0015 + 0.001 + \frac{1}{100} = 0.0158$$
$$U = 1/0.0158 = 63.3 \text{ Btu/(h)(ft}^2)(°F)$$

For the fouled chiller, compute the fouling factor, r_i, by establishing U_F. We had previously calculated $U_F = 10,020/A$. If $A = 338.5 \text{ ft}^2$, then:

$$U_F = 10,020/338.5 = 29.6 \text{ Btu/(h)(ft}^2)(°F)$$

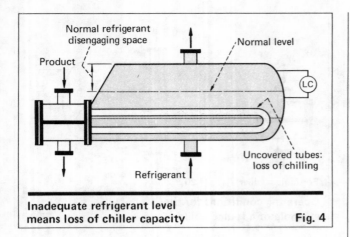

Inadequate refrigerant level
means loss of chiller capacity   Fig. 4

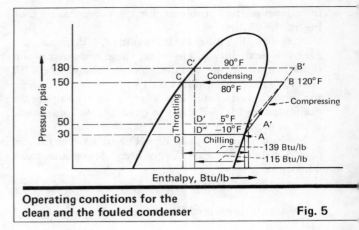

Operating conditions for the
clean and the fouled condenser   Fig. 5

We can now substitute U_F into Eq. (4) in order to compute the r_i for the fouled chiller:

$$(1/29.6) = .0033 + 0.0015 + r_i + 0.01$$
$$r_i = 0.019$$

Hence, the fouling factor went from 0.001 for the clean chiller to 0.019 for the fouled chiller.

If fouling is not the problem with the chiller, then loss of velocity through the chiller can be the cause, or change in viscosity, or level-control effects on the refrigerant side.

Loss of velocity—(we observe a similar problem with an increase in viscosity). Let the new lower velocity $V_N = \frac{1}{2}V_{Design}$. Since the heat-transfer coefficient, h_i or h_o, is a function of diameter, velocity, viscosity, specific heat, thermal conductivity, length, we can focus on velocity and write:

$$h_{iD} = V_D^n f(X) \qquad (5)$$

where h_{iD} is the heat-transfer coefficient at design conditions, V_D^n is velocity at design conditions, and $f(X)$ represents the remaining variables affecting the heat-transfer coefficient. The exponent, n, in Eq. (5) has values of $0.33 \leqslant n \leqslant 0.8$. For turbulent flow, $n = 0.8$. Hence, we can relate the new heat-transfer coefficient, h_{iN}, to the lower velocity as:

$$h_{iN} = (\tfrac{1}{2}V_D)^{0.8} f(X)$$
$$h_{in} = 0.57(V_D)^{0.8} f(X)$$

Substituting the appropriate values for this example into Eq. (4) and using $h_{iN} = 0.57 h_{iD}$, we get:

$$\frac{1}{U} = \frac{1}{300} + 0.0015 + 0.001 + \frac{1}{(100 \times 0.57)} = 0.0233$$
$$U = 1/0.0233 = 42.8 \text{ Btu/(h)(ft}^2)(^{\circ}\text{F)}$$

Hence, the overall heat-transfer coefficient has decreased from 63.3 to 42.8.

Level control—Not maintaining an adequate level in the chiller can result in loss of refrigeration capacity (Fig. 4), as some tubes will not be immersed in refrigerant. Heat removal is most efficient when the refrigerant is liquid. As the refrigerant evaporates, it takes energy in the form of heat from the refrigerant liquid. In turn, this liquid takes heat from the tubes and the process liquid on the inside of the tubes. Therefore, all chiller tubes on the shellside must be covered with refrigerant.

Throttle valves

Problems arising with the throttling valve result in too much or too little refrigerant being fed to the chiller. If too little refrigerant is fed, a loss in refrigeration capacity occurs in a manner similar to that described for level control. If too much refrigerant is fed to the chiller, liquid can build up in the compressor suction drum and eventually get into the compressor suction line. Refrigerant flashing now occurs in places other than the chiller, and refrigeration capacity is reduced.

On occasion, throttle-valve problems can be caused by false or low level in the refrigeration accumulator. Thus, very little liquid and much refrigerant vapor is throttled, and refrigeration capacity is lost.

If the throttle valve is always in the open position (just refrigerant vapor passing through), it is due to the absence of refrigerant liquid in the accumulator. Check the refrigerant level—especially for false level indication due to plugs or icing/hydrate formation.

Fouled condenser

To identify a fouled condenser or loss of condensing capacity, plot the temperature/pressure conditions of the refrigeration cycle. Then, compare the condenser temperature to its design value. A higher condensing temperature indicates condenser problems.

Water condenser—The pressure-enthalpy diagram for a condenser in nonfouled (i.e., clean) and fouled conditions is shown in Fig. 5. On comparing the nonfouled (ABCD in Fig. 5) and fouled (A'B'C'D') cycles, we find the condenser's critical conditions to be:

	Nonfouled	Fouled
Compressor suction:		
Pressure, psia	30	50
Temperature, °F	−10	+5
Compressor discharge:		
Pressure, psia	150	180
Temperature, °F	120	140
Condenser exit:		
Pressure, psia	150	180
Temperature, °F	80	90
Enthalpy difference, ΔH, Btu/lb	139	115

Let us analyze what is happening to the refrigeration cycle during condensing and throttling/chilling on the pressure-enthalpy diagram of Fig. 5.

Condensing: If the accumulator is operating normally, all of the refrigerant in the condenser will con-

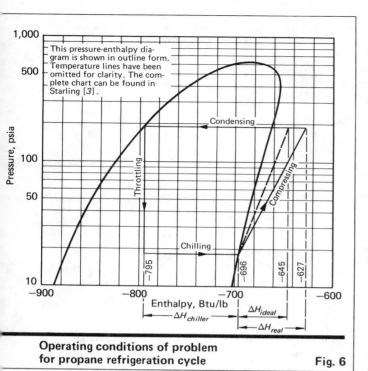

**Operating conditions of problem
for propane refrigeration cycle**   Fig. 6

dense. However, fouling lowers the heat-transfer coefficient, U (as in the case of the chiller, r_o or r_i gets larger due to the fouling film on the shellside or tubeside of the condenser).

As in the chiller case, the duty, q, decreases somewhat due to loss in heat exchange:

$$q_{water} = m_w C_P \Delta T \qquad (6)$$

where m_w = mass flowrate of water, lb/h; C_p = specific heat of water = 1, Btu/(lb)(°F); and ΔT = temperature difference of water, °F.

As ΔT decreases and all other variables remain constant, q decreases. Eq. (3) relates q and U. Since q and U have decreased, the (LMTD) must increase to restore equilibrium. An increase in the (LMTD) means an increase in condensing temperature, and the refrigerant is now on line B'C' on Fig. 5.

The Point C' is the new refrigerant saturated liquid boundary. Initially, throttling will take place along line C'D''. However, the enthalpy available has decreased from 139 to 115 Btu/lb. To compensate, more refrigerant has to be fed to the chiller (mass flowrate compensates for energy loss). The pressure in the chiller increases and the new refrigeration cycle is A'B'C'D. Only subcooling could decrease C' to C in order to achieve a ΔH of 139 Btu/lb.

Air condenser—Loss of capacity in an air condenser occurs in the same manner as for a water condenser but for different reasons. The basic reason is a decreased airflow across the tubes, which may be caused by:
■ Fouled finned-tubes, caused by debris.
■ Clogged inlet screens.
■ Incorrect action of the air louvers.
■ Improper pitch of the fan blades.
■ Wrong speed of rotation for the fan.
■ Excessive clearance of the blade tips.

Loss of air around the condenser tubes affects U due to a decrease in air velocity, but a reduction in the mass flow of air causes the exit air temperature to rise. Hence, the (LMTD) increases, and the same abnormal refrigeration cycle as in the water condenser takes place (i.e., similar to the cycle A'B'C'D' of Fig. 5).

Compressor problems

In many instances when a complex problem with a refrigeration system cannot be identified, the compressor is blamed. Definite assurance that the driver and not the compressor causes the problem can save money and downtime in tearing down the compressor.

Compressor efficiency and horsepower consumption are the two key items for evaluating compressor and driver operation. The easiest way to find compressor efficiency and horsepower draw is to plot them on a pressure-enthalpy diagram.

Let us assume the following conditions for propane refrigerant: suction pressure and temperature are 18 psia and −20°F, respectively; discharge pressure and suction are 189 psia and 165°F. To prepare diagram:
1. Plot the complete refrigeration cycle (Fig. 6).
2. Notice that the actual compression line does not follow the isentropic line. In Fig. 6, the true isentropic line is shown dashed.
3. Consider that an accurate compression line must include the pressure drop at both suction and discharge. (On Fig. 6, this is difficult to do.) Typical suction and discharge pressure drops are: 3 to 5 psi for reciprocating compressors, and 1 psi for all other types.

To determine the compressor adiabatic efficiency, η_C, solve:

$$\eta_C = \frac{\Delta H_I}{\Delta H_R} \qquad (7)$$

where ΔH_I is the ideal change in enthalpy between suction and discharge conditions, plotted along the isentropic line (dashed line in Fig. 6), and ΔH_R is the difference in enthalpies between suction and discharge at actual compressor conditions (solid line in Fig. 6).

Note: An accurate compression line should account for suction/discharge pressure losses. A 5-psi drop should suffice for the pressure line.

For our example, the efficiency becomes:

$$\eta_C = \frac{-645 - (-696)}{-627 - (-696)} = \frac{51}{69} = 0.74$$

Typical compressor adiabatic efficiencies are:

Reciprocating	0.85 to 0.95
Screw	0.80 to 0.85
Centrifugal	0.70 to 0.75

If our compressor is a centrifugal, it is running at its correct efficiency. When compressor efficiency is low, we should look for:
■ Open unloading pockets, or leaking internal valves. Such leaks are serious because the discharge temperature gets extremely high, and the system may burn out. The compression line in this case diverges excessively from the isentropic line, and ΔH_R gets very high.
■ Extreme ambient conditions.
■ Cylinder wear on reciprocating compressors, or wear on labyrinth seals or wheels on centrifugals.

■ Faulty bypass valves on suction and discharge.

■ Compressor driver problems. To verify that the driver is operating correctly, we must determine the ideal horsepower, obtain the design horsepower and calculate the horsepower draw ratio for the compressor from the following:

$$(HP)_{d.r.} = (HP)_I/(HP)_D \qquad (8)$$

where $(HP)_{d.r.}$ is the horsepower draw ratio, $(HP)_I$ is ideal horsepower (i.e., horsepower drawn during compressor operation), and $(HP)_D$ is the nameplate (i.e., design) horsepower.

We determine the ideal horsepower for:

a. Electric-motor drivers, from:

$$(HP)_I = EI\,\eta_m/746 \qquad (9)$$

where E is voltage, V; I is current, A; η_m is motor efficiency; and 746 W = 1 hp.

b. Other drivers (steam turbines, etc.), from:

$$(HP)_I = M_R\,\Delta H_C/2{,}545 \qquad (10)$$

where M_R is the refrigerant circulation rate, lb/h; ΔH_C is the compressor enthalpy rise, Btu/lb; and 2,545 Btu/h = 1 hp.

The compressor enthalpy, ΔH_C, is found from Fig. 6 where $\Delta H_{chiller} = \Delta H_C$:

$$\Delta H_C = -696 - (-795) = 99 \text{ Btu/lb}$$

To find the refrigeration circulation rate, M_R, might be more difficult depending on whether there is a flowmeter on the line. Be sure that the flowmeter is working correctly and is placed to record single-phase flow.

Let us now consider another way for determining the refrigeration rate. The heat taken up by the refrigerant in the chiller is equal to the heat removed from the process, or:

$$q_{process} = q_{refrig.}$$

To determine the heat removed from the process, we must evaluate:

$$q_{process} = \sum_{i=1}^{k} [M_{gas,i} \times H_{gas,i}^n + M_{liq,i} \times H_{liq,i}^n - (m_{gas,i} \times H_{liq,i}^{n'} + m_{liq,i} \times H_{liq,i}^{n'})] \qquad (11)$$

where M_i or m_i is the mass flowrate into (M) or out of (m) the chiller in liquid or gaseous phase for chiller i; H_i^n is the enthalpy of the process fluid at $n°$F for chiller i; and k is the k-th chiller (i.e., the summation is for all chillers in service).

To determine the heat taken up by refrigerant, we evaluate:

$$q_{refrig.} = M_R\Delta H_C \qquad (12)$$

where M_R is the refrigerant circulation rate, lb/h, and ΔH_C is the compressor enthalpy rise, Btu/lb.

Since our earlier example had a $\Delta H_C = 99$ Btu/lb, we can write an equation for the refrigerant circulation rate in terms of ΔH_C as:

$$M_R = q_{refrig.}/99 = q_{process}/99 \qquad (13)$$

Let us work out an example for two chillers operating under the following conditions:

Chiller 1:

	Flow, lb/h	Enthalpy, Btu/lb	Temperature, °F
M_{gas}	4,806	152	60
$M_{liq.}$	5,447	−25	60
m_{gas}	1,395	150	0
$m_{liq.}$	8,858	−57	0

Chiller 2:

	Flow, lb/h	Enthalpy, Btu/lb	Temperature, °F
M_{gas}	34,773	127	39
$M_{liq.}$	—	—	—
m_{gas}	34,773	−18	25
$m_{liq.}$	—	—	—

The duty for Chillers 1 and 2 is calculated from:

$$q_{Chiller\ 1} = 4{,}806(152) + 5{,}447(-25) - [1{,}395(150) + 8{,}858(-57)]$$

$$= 889{,}993 \text{ Btu/h}$$

$$q_{Chiller\ 2} = 34{,}773[127 - (-18)] = 5{,}042{,}085 \text{ Btu/h}$$

$$q_{process} = \sum_{i=1}^{2} q_{Chiller\ i} = 5{,}932{,}078 \text{ Btu/h}$$

Substituting into Eq. (13), we find the refrigeration recirculation rate, M_R, to be:

$$M_R = 5{,}932{,}078/99 \simeq 59{,}920 \text{ lb/h}$$

Using this value in Eq. (10), we establish the ideal horsepower for this example as:

$$(HP)_I = 59{,}920(51)/2{,}545 \simeq 1{,}201 \text{ hp}$$

If the driver for this installation is designed for 1,500 hp, we find the horsepower draw ratio from Eq. (8) as:

$$(HP)_{d.r.} = 1{,}201/1{,}500 \simeq 0.80$$

Normally, the $(HP)_{d.r.}$ is between 0.75 and 0.85. Hence, for this example, the compressor driver is operating correctly.

References

1. "Engineering Data Book," 9th ed., Gas Processors Suppliers Assn. [formerly Natural Gas Processors Suppliers Assn.], Tulsa, Okla., 1972.
2. Canjar, L., and Manning, F., "Thermodynamic Properties & Reduced Correlations for Gases," Gulf Publishing, Houston, 1967.
3. Starling, K. E., "Fluid Thermodynamic Properties for Light Petroleum Systems," Gulf Publishing, Houston, 1973.
4. Young, V. W., and Young, G. A., "Elementary Engineering Thermodynamics," McGraw-Hill, New York, 1941.
5. "Gas Technology Notes," Canadian Natural Gas Processors Assn., Calgary, Alta., Canada, 1975.

The author

Kenneth J. Vargas is an operations engineer at the Rimbey Operations of Gulf Canada Resources Inc., P.O. Box 530, Rimbey, AB T0C 2J0, Canada. A graduate of the U.S. Air Force Academy with a B.Sc. in mathematics and mechanics, he has previously worked in process and maintenance engineering for Eldorado Nuclear Ltd. Canada and Du Pont Mexico.

Refrigeration systems for low-temperature processes

Understanding the thermodynamics of the vapor-compression cycle provides the basis for practical design of actual refrigeration units. Here is detailed information for designing single-stage, multistage and cascaded systems.

Yuv R. Mehra, *El Paso Hydrocarbons Co.*

☐ Refrigeration systems are common in processes related to the petroleum-refining, petrochemical and chemical industries. The selection of a refrigerant is generally based upon its availability and cooling range, and previous experience with it.

For instance, in an olefins plant, pure ethylene and propylene are readily available; whereas in a natural-gas processing plant, ethane and propane are at hand. Propane or propylene may not be suitable in an ammonia plant because of the risk of contamination, while ammonia may very well serve the purpose. Fluorocarbons have been used extensively because of their non-flammable characteristics.

Due to their inherent properties, a variety of refrigerants as listed in Table I are used quite economically over a wide range of cooling temperatures.

All types of compressors—reciprocating, screw and centrifugal—are used for refrigeration services. The theory of refrigeration can be applied to any compressor, but side loads are usually considered only in centrifugal compressors. Hence, we will confine our discussion to centrifugal machines.

The refrigeration effect can be achieved by using one of the following cycles: (a) vapor compression (reversed Carnot), (b) expansion (reversed Brayton), (c) absorption, and (d) steam jet (water-vapor compression). All of these cycles have been used successfully in industrial refrigeration, but the majority of installations use vapor compression. Therefore, we shall discuss only the reversed Carnot cycle.

Thermodynamics of cycles

A Carnot cycle is composed of two isothermal and two isentropic processes, as represented on the temperature-entropy (T-S) and the pressure-enthalpy (P-H) diagrams in Fig. 1a. Here, Process 1-2 represents expan-

sion or pressure reduction; Process 2-3 represents heat rejection at constant temperature; Process 3-4 represents compression or increase in pressure; and Process 4-1 completes the cycle by heat addition at constant temperature. To carry out a Carnot cycle, it is necessary to have an ideal fluid.

However, real cycles, both direct and reverse, operate with fluids that undergo phase changes during the cycles. It is important to recognize that real processes transfer heat at essentially constant pressure instead of constant temperature.

A vapor-compression or a reversed Carnot cycle includes the same processes that occur during the expansion of a fluid in the direct Carnot cycle but in a reversed order. This cycle can be represented on T-S and P-H diagrams, as shown in Fig. 1b.

Vapor-compression cycle

A vapor-compression cycle can also be represented by hooking up equipment in the sequence shown in Fig. 2a. In order to illustrate the processes involved in this refrigeration cycle, let us consider each step:

Expansion process—The expansion process, Point 1 to Point 2 (1-2) in Fig. 2a, can also be referred to as an isenthalpic process. In a refrigeration cycle, it can be accomplished by flashing the liquid refrigerant through a control or expansion valve. The process can be represented on a P-H diagram, as in Fig. 2b.

Every refrigerant has its own P-H diagram that represents all thermodynamic properties. From a refrigeration standpoint, the envelope formed by the bubble-point curve and the dew-point curve joining each other at the critical point is very important.

The area left of the bubble-point curve represents subcooled liquid refrigerant; the area between the bubble-point and dew-point curves represents the presence

Originally published July 12, 1982

Sizing Line C to handle the minimum holding load

Table IV

Item	Minimum load, small riser ($-22°$ F)		
	1-in. Sched. 40	1½-in. Sched. 40	2-in. Sched. 40
Tons, evaporator	2	2	2
Density liq., lb/ft^3	92.89	92.89	92.89
Lb/min, liq.	25.419	25.419	25.419
Density vapor, lb/ft^3	0.39173	0.39173	0.39173
Lb/min, vapor	5.627	5.627	5.627
I.D., ft	0.8740	0.13420	0.17220
A_x, ft^2	0.00600	0.01414	0.02330
μ_l, centipoise	0.3750	0.3750	0.3750
μ_v, centipoise	0.01015	0.01015	0.01015
μ_l, lb/ft-hr	0.9075	0.9075	0.9075
μ_v, lb/ft-hr	0.024563	0.024563	0.024563
B_x	78.71	78.71	78.71
B_y	20,149	8,549.8	5,118.6
Type flow	Annular	Annular	Slug
DG/μ, vapor	200,220	130,452	101,584
ϵ	0.00015	0.00015	0.00015
ϵ/D	0.001716	0.001118	0.00087
f, vapor	0.0231	0.0222	0.0218
Velocity, ft/s (vapor)	39.9	16.98	10.275
ΔP/100 ft, ft fluid	653.37	74.06	20.754
ΔP/100 ft, psi (vapor)	1.78	0.2015	0.0565
DG/μ, liq.	24,481	15,950	12,421
f, liq.	0.0283	0.0296	0.0302
Velocity, ft/s (liq.)	0.76	0.3225	0.1957
ΔP/100 ft, ft fluid	0.2905	0.03562	0.010434
ΔP/100 ft, psi (liq.)	0.1874	0.02298	0.00673
$x = \sqrt{\dfrac{\Delta P_{l-100}}{\Delta P_{v-100}}}$ =	0.3245	0.3377	0.345
a (annular) =	4.4722	4.29688	4.15406
b (annular) =	0.32097	0.30919	0.29959
$\phi = ax^b$ =	3.116	3.0717	
$\phi = \dfrac{1{,}190\,x^{0.815}}{(W_l/A)^{0.5}}$ =			1.954
2-Phase ΔP, psi/100 ft			
$\phi^2 \cdot \Delta P_v$	17.283	1.901	0.216 ΔP
$-22°$ F, psia	14.56	14.56	Note: Slug flow gives excessive static head
C 2-Phase ΔP, psi	4.29	0.65	
K Pressure, psia	10.27	13.91	
K Temperature, °F	-36.2	-23.9	
Temperature penalty, °F	14.2	1.9	> 30.0

Note: A size 1¼-in. line would give approx: $\left(\dfrac{1.61}{1.38}\right)^5 \times 1.901 = 4.11$ psi/100 ft (N.G.)

the evaporator, one can integrate the temperature-pressure-density variations for each refrigerant and calculate the required temperature level at the top of the liquid column. Then one could determine the capacity and power penalty requirements of a two-stage compressor system to handle the refrigeration load as compared to a situation where there was no more than the normally-allowed 3°F suction riser penalty. The results are shown in Table I.

Obviously, the static-head penalty has to be reduced by some means. Also, the two-phase pressure drop must be controlled within a reasonable amount.

Two-phase pressure drop

A convenient method of calculating pressure drop substitutes an equivalent length of straight pipe or tubing for each fitting or valve. Then one determines the total pressure drops of the various straight lengths. For single-phase flow with either liquid or gas, the Moody data [2] are appropriate.

For two-phase flow there can be at least seven patterns of flow, as defined by Kern [4].

Many academic methods have been proposed for determining two-phase pressure drop. The Lockhart-Martinelli [3] method will generally provide conservative sizing (or oversizing) of lines larger than about 1-in. nominal pipe size. For a method that gives relatively fast answers that are not overly conservative, and correlate with some experience on actual refrigeration systems, the reader is referred to the Baker map and the procedure of Kern [4,8] for the sizing of single pipes. For small increments of temperature change, the evaluation of pressure drop is essentially isothermal and will not lead to significant error.

Single riser sizing

A single vertical riser sized for minimum pressure-drop at full flow of vapor (full refrigeration load) would produce an excessive liquid-refrigerant static-head penalty on the refrigeration system at greatly reduced loads. Also, at greatly reduced loads and low vapor velocities in the single large line, the probability of adequate oil return to the refrigeration plant is diminished.

On the other hand, a single riser sized for high vapor-velocity at greatly reduced load would be counterproductive. It would assure dispersed or annular flow (so that static-head penalty would be eliminated and so that there would be adequate oil return), but it would result in an excessive pressure-loss penalty at high loads.

Why dual risers are needed

What is really needed is a piping network that permits optimum velocities and pressure drops, as well as effective oil return, at all load conditions. These features are provided by a trapped large line and a smaller vapor-bleed line upstream of the trap, such as depicted in Fig. 2. Both lines conduct flow at maximum load. At a greatly reduced load, the large trapped line D is sealed by trapped liquids, and vapor flows through the smaller line C.

This concept has been used for many years to move oil up hot gas-discharge lines or suction lines that undergo wide variation in loading, when conventional single-phase refrigerant flow is employed. The actual sizing method practiced varies with the individual; the literature is somewhat vague and subject to interpretation. Hitherto, much was left to the judgment and experience of the individual designer.

However, a more scientific approach is essential if the method is to be applied with confidence to liquid-overfeed systems using a wide range of refrigerants and other fluids. This article has been written to achieve that end.

In the following example, much use is made of Ref. [1 – 6]. A further refinement, that may prove quite a challenge, could be pursued using adaptations from the work of DeGance and Atherton [7] particularly for the system piping. However, quite satisfactory results for the sizing of dual suction risers can be obtained by using the concept proposed in this example.

Sizing for minimum load

A batch-cooling load followed by a tapering holding load might be as shown in Table II.

This particular plant uses R-12 refrigerant; the vertical rise, h, of Fig. 2 is 12 ft, a maximum of 3°F temperature-penalty of the riser was permitted, and the piping is Schedule 40 black steel. The header K-L-B (Fig. 2) was sized for about 3°F temperature-penalty back to the accumulator. It was assumed that the liquid pump would deliver the liquid to the evaporator at essentially the evaporator outlet-temperature level, because of added pump-motor heat and heat pickup through insulation, with negligible pressure-drop in the evaporator itself. Therefore, the lb/min of vapor is based on the latent heat at the evaporator outlet.

At −15°F, the pressure of R-12 is 17.14 psia; density of liquid is 92.19 lb/ft³; sp. vol. of saturated vapor is 2.1923 ft³/lb; latent heat is 70.3514 Btu/lb; viscosity of liquid is 0.8833 lb/ft-h, or 0.365 centipoise; viscosity of vapor is 0.024926 lb/ft-h, or 0.0103 centipoise; and the surface tension of the liquid is 16 dynes/cm.

At −22°F, the pressure of R-12 is 14.56 psia; density of liquid is 92.89 lb/ft³; sp. vol. of saturated vapor is 2.5528 ft³/lb; latent heat is 71.081 Btu/lb; viscosity of liquid is 0.9075 lb/ft-h, or 0.375 centipoise, viscosity of vapor is 0.024563 lb/ft-h, or 0.01015 centipoise, and the surface tension is 16.5 dynes/cm.

Holding at −22°F

At maximum: 4.1 tons:

$$2.5 \times \frac{92.89}{7.48} = 31.046 \text{ lb/min liquid feed}$$

$$\frac{4.1 \times 200}{71.081} = 11.536 \text{ lb/min evaporated and}$$
returned as vapor via vertical risers

$$31.046 - 11.536 =$$
19.51 lb/min liquid returned via vertical risers

At minimum: 2 tons:

$$\frac{2 \times 200}{71.081} = 5.627 \text{ lb/min evaporated and}$$
returned as vapor via vertical risers

$$31.046 - 5.627 =$$
25.419 lb/min liquid returned via vertical risers

Determining flow and pressure drop in each "pair" of risers

Table V

	Pair I		Pair II	
	C 1½ in. (small)	D 2½ in. (large)	C 1½ in. (small)	D 3 in. (large)
Temperature, °F	-15	-15	-15	-15
Lb/min vapor	12.362	33.124	8.350	37.136
Lb/min liquid	4.386	11.752	2.962	13.176
ρ_l lb/ft^3	92.19	92.19	92.19	92.19
ρ_v lb/ft^3	0.4562	0.4562	0.4562	0.4562
μ_l, centipoise	0.365	0.365	0.365	0.365
σ_l, dynes/cm	16	16	16	16
W_l/W_v	0.355	0.355	0.355	0.355
B_x	2.676	2.676	2.676	2.676
A_x, ft^2	0.01414	0.03322	0.01414	0.05130
I.D., ft	0.1342	0.2057	0.1342	0.2557
W_v/A	52,456	59,827	35,431	43,434
$2.16/\sqrt{\rho_l \rho_v}$	0.3331	0.3331	0.3331	0.3331
B_y	17,472	19,927	11,801	14,467
Flow	Annular	Annular	Annular	Annular
I.D., in.	1.61	2.469	1.61	3.068
a	4.2969	4.0284	4.2969	3.8413
b	0.30919	0.29115	0.30919	0.27857
μ_l, lb/ft-hr	0.8833	0.8833	0.8833	0.8833
μ_v, lb/ft-hr	0.024926	0.024926	0.024926	0.024926
ϵ/D	0.0011177	0.000729	0.001117	0.000587
DG/μ, vapor	282,417	493,715	190,760	445,561
f_v	0.021	0.019	0.0212	0.0181
Vapor velocity, ft/s	31.94	36.43	21.57	26.45
$\Delta P/100$ ft, ft vapor	247.9	190.35	114.1	76.9
$\Delta P/100$ ft, psi	0.785	0.603	0.362	0.244
DG/μ, liq.	2,828	4,943	1,910	4,461
f_l	0.0222 to 0.0445	0.0382	0.033	0.0395
Liq. velocity, ft/s	0.05608	0.06396	0.03787	0.04643
$\Delta P/100$ ft, ft liq.	0.000808 to 0.001619	0.00118	0.0005476	0.0005171
Liq. $\Delta P/100$ ft, psi	0.000517 to 0.001037	0.0007555	0.0003506	0.00033105
$x = \sqrt{\dfrac{\Delta P_{l-100}}{\Delta P_{v-100}}} =$	0.02566 to 0.03635	0.0354	0.03112	0.03683
$\phi = ax^b =$	1.385 to 1.542	1.523	1.4697	1.5313
2-Phase ΔP, psi/100 ft $\phi^2 \cdot \Delta P_{v-100} =$	1.506 to 1.87	1.399	0.782	0.572
2-Phase ΔP, total psi	0.512 to 0.636	0.684	0.266	0.332
P at -15°F, psia	17.14	17.14	17.14	17.14
P at K and L	16.50	16.46	16.87	16.81
T at K and L, °F	-16.7	-16.8	-15.7	-15.9
Temperature penalty, °F	1.7	1.8	0.7	0.9

C = 1½ in.
D = 2½ in.
Adequate

C = 1½ in.
D = 3 in.
Has ~ 1°F less penalty

Pulldown

At 16 tons:

$$5 \times \frac{92.19}{7.48} = 61.624 \text{ lb/min liquid feed}$$

For the purpose of this analysis it is assumed that the turbulent condition of the flow causes equal liquid-vapor ratios in lines C and D. Once flow is established through D, at start of pulldown, D continues to conduct vapor and liquid flow even at lower loads until liquid flow is interrupted or the momentum of liquid and vapor is significantly reduced to that existing near the minimum holding load.

There is an equivalent-length difference between circuits F-K and F-G-L, and this should be considered. The solution to the problem of sizing C and D involves trial assumptions of flows in each until the 2-phase pressure-drops in each circuit balance. To simplify the calculations, the assumptions shown in Table III were made.

The first task is to size Line C to handle the minimum holding load under an annular or dispersed-flow condition, which would assure lack of static-head penalty. To do this, the Baker map [4, 8] should be examined. Moody's friction-factor curves must be referred to [2]. The calculations are shown in Table IV. It is therefore determined that a nominal size $1\frac{1}{2}$-in. Schedule 40 pipe for Circuit C is optimum for the minimum holding load.

Now, at a pulldown load of 16 tons, determine the size of the Line D. Assume equal liquid-vapor ratio for C and D. An approximate relationship of flows in C and D is determined by the equation:

$$\text{lb/min, } C = \frac{\text{lb/min total vapor or liquid}}{1 + \left[\left(\frac{\text{I.D.}D}{\text{I.D.}C}\right)^{2.73} \times \left(\frac{\text{equiv. length } C}{\text{equiv. length } D}\right)^{0.5}\right]}$$

(Total vapor = 45.486 lb/min and total liquid = 16.138 lb/min)

With $1\frac{1}{2}$ in. Schedule 40 at 1.610″ I.D. and 34.0 ft equivalent length for Line C, then evaluate the quantity of vapor and liquid in Lines C and D for two sizes of D.

Pipe size, in.	I.D., in.	Equiv. length, ft	Vapor Lb/min, C	Vapor Lb/min, D	Liquid Lb/min, C	Liquid Lb/min, D
$2\frac{1}{2}$	2.469	48.9(D)	12.362	33.124	4.386	11.752
3	3.068	58.1(D)	8.350	37.136	2.962	13.176

The type of flow must be determined for each "pair" of risers in each circuit and appropriate equations used for the pressure drop. These calculations are shown in Table V.

Conclusion

One can use a $1\frac{1}{2}$-in. pipe for C and $2\frac{1}{2}$-in. for D, although a $1\frac{1}{2}$-in. for C and 3-in. for D would have the lowest penalty.

With $1\frac{1}{2}$-in. and 3-in. risers, the two extremes of loading produce 1.9°F to 0.8°F penalty on the evaporator. At the beginning of pulldown, Riser D begins to conduct vapor and liquid and continues to do so at lower pulldown loads, until some time during the holding mode when the single riser, C, carries all the liquid and vapor. If this occurs at maximum holding load, the temperature penalty by calculation is 4.4°F maximum. It is difficult to calculate precisely just when Riser C "takes over" completely, because so much depends on the sustained momentum of the fluids. If loads gradually increase from a minimum, the point at which D begins to conduct flow would be at a higher load than where D ceases to conduct on falling load. The relative physical location of parts F and G influence the "cut-in" and "cut-out" points of Line D. G should be immediately adjacent to F.

Summary

Fig. 1 shows a few applications that use the flexibility and efficient operation made possible with liquid-overfeed refrigeration systems. By using dual risers, excessive static-head or excessive two-phase pressure-drop penalties are eliminated for all situations from maximum to minimum load. Also, close control of product temperatures and effective oil return are realized.

The conceptual approach described here for sizing the dual risers for these systems has been successful in assuring minimum temperature penalty, optimum oil return and maximum potential for operating-cost savings in refrigeration systems.

References

1. American Soc. of Heating, Refrigerating and Air Conditioning Engineers, "ASHRAE Handbook of Fundamentals," Chap. 4, 16, 32, ASHRAE, New York, N.Y., 1977.

2. Moody, Lewis F., Friction Factors for Pipe Flow, *Trans. ASME (Am. Soc. Mech. Eng.*, pp. 671–684 (1944).

3. Lockhart, R. W., and Martinelli, R. C., Proposed Correlation of Data for Isothermal Two-Phase, Two-Component Flow in Pipes, *Chem. Eng. Prog.*, Vol. 45, No. 1, pp. 39–48.

4. Kern, Robert, How to Size Process Piping for Two-Phase Flow, *Hydrocarbon Process.*, Oct. 1969, pp. 105–116.

5. Crane Co., "Flow of Fluids Through Valves, Fittings, and Pipe," Crane Technical Paper No. 410.

6. American Soc. of Heating, Refrigerating and Air Conditioning Engineers, "ASHRAE Handbook of Systems," Chap. 25 and 26, ASHRAE, New York, 1976.

7. DeGance, Anthony E., and Atherton, Robert W., Chemical Engineering Aspects of Two-Phase Flow, Parts 1–8, *Chem. Eng.*, Mar. 23, Apr. 20, May 4, July 13, Aug. 10, Oct. 5, Nov. 2, 1970 and Feb. 22, 1971.

8. Kern, Robert, Piping Design for Two-Phase Flow, *Chem. Eng.*, June 23, 1975, pp. 145–151.

The author

Donald K. Miller is Chief Engineer, Absorption and Reciprocating Compressors Development, York Div. of Borg-Warner Corp., P.O. Box 1592, York, PA 17405, where he is involved in guiding development, manufacture, application and construction of refrigeration components and systems. He holds a BSChE from the University of Missouri, is a registered professional engineer in Pennsylvania, and is a member of the American Soc. of Heating, Refrigeration and Air Conditioning Engineers and Vice-Chairman of the Air-Conditioning and Refrigeration Institute's Reciprocating Liquid-Chilling Packages Engineering Committee.

Variable fan speeds cut cooling-tower operating costs

Regulating the air flow through cooling towers by controlling fan speed via a.c. adjustable-speed drives can significantly reduce power costs, lessen maintenance expenses and extend equipment life.

James D. Johnson, General Electric Co.

☐ With electricity at 6¢/kWh, a typical mechanical-draft cooling tower with a 75-hp fan in continuous operation, driven by an a.c. induction motor, generates a power bill of nearly $32,000/yr (75 hp × 0.746 kW/hp × 8,760 h/yr × $0.06/kWh × 1/0.92 efficiency = $31,964/yr).

Because fan hp rating is based on required air flow for worst-case wet- and dry-bulb temperatures (which occur only a small part of a year), air flow—hence, power cost—can be reduced, over 50% in many cases, while cooling is still maintained.

Fig. 1 shows the relationship between air flow (ft³/min) and power for centrifugal fans. Note that the required driving hp declines rapidly as air flow is reduced. For centrifugal fans, the fan law states that flow is proportional to fan speed, and power required is proportional to speed cubed. Therefore, slower fan speeds result in large reductions in power requirements.

Savings from adjusting fan speed

Adjustable-speed operation of cooling-tower fans has been made practical by recently developed inverter power units, which have made variable-speed operation of standard induction motors reliable and cost-effective. Such operation can result in significant savings in electrical power costs, reduced water wind-drift loss, longer mechanical-equipment life, and less noise and vibration.

One method of accurately evaluating the possible en-

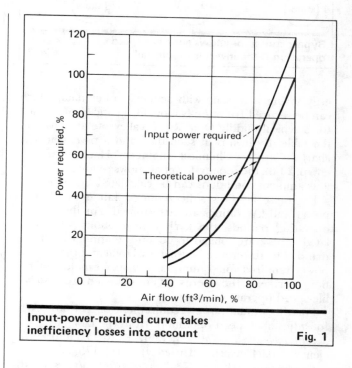

Input-power-required curve takes inefficiency losses into account

Fig. 1

Operating data for southern Ohio cooling tower, with 75-hp fan motor						
Operating time, h	Average ambient temperature, °F	Wet-bulb temperature, °F	Required air flow, ft³/min	Fan motor size, hp	Motor rating, kW	Power usage, kWh
22	97	76	275,728	73.8	55.0	1,210
378	92	74	256,818	59.6	44.5	16,821
1,837	77	68	214,359	34.7	25.9	47,578
2,380	62	57	171,135	17.6	13.2	31,416
1,973	47	43	140,891	10.0	7.5	14,798
1,706	32	30	122,985	6.6	4.9	8,359
464	13	12	106,222	4.3	3.2	1,485
8,760						121,667

Originally published August 8, 1983

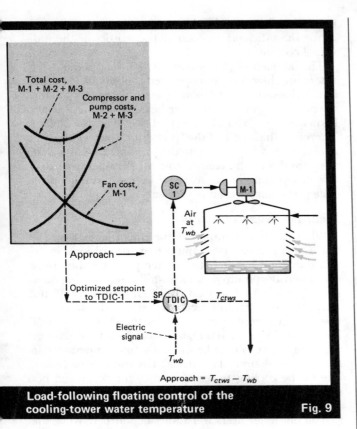

Load-following floating control of the cooling-tower water temperature   Fig. 9

mum, identifying the optimum approach that allows operation at an overall minimum cost. This ΔT automatically becomes the setpoint of TDIC-1. This optimum approach increases if the load on the cooling tower increases or if the wet-bulb temperature decreases.

If the cooling-tower fans have variable-speed drives, then the optimum approach is maintained by throttling. If the tower fans are two-speed or single-speed units, then the output of TDIC-1 incrementally starts and stops the fans to maintain the optimum approach.

Where a large number of cooling-tower cells comprise the total system, the water flowrates to the various cells should be automatically balanced as a function of the operation of the associated fan. In other words, flows to all cells whose fans are at high speed should be kept at identical high rates, while cells with low-speed fans should receive water at equal low flows. Cells with their fans off should be supplied with water at a minimum flowrate.

T_{ctwr} optimization

Fig. 10 shows that the combined cost of operating the cooling-tower pumps and the chiller compressor is a function of the temperature rise across the condenser. Because an increase in this rise increases compression costs while decreasing pumping costs, the combined cost curve has a minimum point. The ΔT corresponding to this minimum automatically becomes the setpoint of TDIC-1 in the optimized control loop in Fig. 10.

This controller is the cascade master of PDIC-1, which guarantees that the pressure difference between the supply and return cooling-tower water flowrates is enough to provide flow through the users, but never enough to

cause damage. The high and low limits are set on HLL-1. TDIC-1 freely floats this setpoint within these limits to keep the operating cost at a minimum.

To protect against reset windup (when the output of TDIC-1 reaches one of these limits), an external feedback is provided from the PDIC-1 output signal.

When the cooling-tower-water pump station consists of several pumps, and only one is variable-speed, pump increments are started when PSH-1 signals that the pump-speed controller setpoint is at its maximum. When the load is dropping, the excess pump increments are stopped on the basis of *flow*, as detected by FSL-2. To eliminate cycling, the excess pump increment is turned off only when the actual total flow corresponds to less than 90% of the capacity of the *remaining* pumps.

This load-following optimization loop floats the total cooling-tower water flowrate to achieve maximum overall economy. To maintain efficient heat transfer and good turbulence in the condenser, a small local circulating pump P-1, is provided at the condenser. This pump is started and stopped by FSLH-3, guaranteeing that the water velocity in the condenser tubes will never drop below the adjustable limit of, say, 4 ft/s. (This is the same strategy used for the evaporator in Fig. 8.)

Other chiller optimization methods

The controls described in Fig. 7–10 automatically minimize the operating cost of the refrigeration machine as a single integrated system. Additional steps toward reducing operating costs include:

If storage tanks are available, it is economical to produce the daily brine or chilled-water needs of the plant at night, when it is least expensive to do so. At night, ambient temperatures are lower, and electricity is less expensive in some areas.

Since, in a typical plant, coolant can be provided from many sources, another approach is to restructure the system in response to changes in loads, ambient conditions, and utility costs. For example, at some operating and ambient conditions, the cooling-tower water may be cold enough to meet the demands of the process directly. Alternatively, if the cooling-tower outflow is below the temperature required by the process, the chillers can be operated in a thermosiphon mode. Refrigerant circulation is then driven by the temperature differential rather than by a compressor.

When demand is low, it may be possible to save money by operating the chillers part-time at peak efficiency, rather than steadily at partial loading. Efficiency tends to be low at partial loads, because of losses caused by friction drop across suction dampers, pre-rotation vanes, and steam governors. Cycling is practical if the storage capacity of the distribution headers is large enough to avoid frequent stops and starts. For intermittent operation, data such as the heat to be removed and the characteristics of the available chillers are needed to determine the most economical operating strategy.

When chiller cycling is used, the thermal capacity of the chilled-water distribution system absorbs the load while the chiller is off. For example, a pipe distribution network with a volume of 100,000 gal represents a thermal capacity of about 1 million Btu for each degree of temperature rise. If the chilled-water temperature may

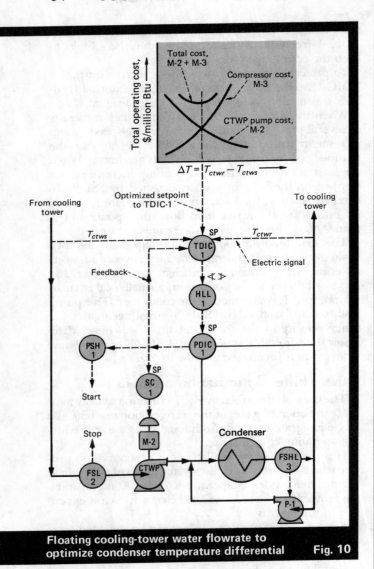

Floating cooling-tower water flowrate to optimize condenser temperature differential   **Fig. 10**

boilers, this accounts for differences among units, as well as for the efficiency-vs.-load characteristics of the individual coolant sources.

The last step of chiller optimization is applicable only where the chillers are not operated continuously. In such installations, the optimization system "knows" before startup how much heat must be removed, and it also knows the size and efficiency of the available chillers. Therefore the length of the "pull-down" period (the time to pull down temperature to the process setpoint) can be minimized and the energy cost of this operation optimized. Optimization is achieved by not starting up the chiller any sooner than is necessary.

Heat-recovery controls

When the heat pumped by the chiller is recovered as hot water, the required optimizing control loop is depicted in Fig. 11. The hot-water temperature also can be continuously optimized in a load-following floating manner. If, at a particular load, 100°F instead of 120°F hot water is sufficient, this technique allows the same tonnage of refrigeration to be met by the chiller at a 30% lower cost. The reason is that the compressor's discharge pressure is determined by the hot-water temperature in the split condenser. This device has two sets of coils—one to the cooling tower, the other for recovered hot water. It can be run either way.

The optimization control loop in Fig. 11 guarantees that all hot-water users will always be satisfied, while the water temperature is minimized. TY-1 selects the most-open hot-water valve, and VPC-1 compares its transmitter signal to a 90% setpoint. If even the most-open valve is less than 90% open, the setpoint of TIC-1 is decreased; while if it exceeds 90%, the setpoint is increased. Thereby a condition is maintained such that all users are able to obtain more heat (by further opening their supply valves) if needed, while the header temperature is continuously optimized.

Fig. 11 also shows that an increasing demand for heat will cause the TIC-1 output signal to rise as its measurement drops below its setpoint. An increase in heat load will cause a decrease in the heat spill to the cooling tower, as the control valve TCV-1A is closed between 3 and 9 psi (typical range for pneumatic split-range valves). At a 9 psi output-signal, all the available cooling load is being recovered and TCV-1A is fully closed. If the heat load continues to rise (the TIC-1 output signal rises over 9 psi) this results in the partial opening of the "pay heat" valve, TCV-1B. Pay heat means that it has to be paid for, i.e., bought from an outside source. In this mode of operation, steam heat is used to supplement the freely available recovered heat.

A local circulating pump P-1 is started whenever the flow velocity is low, to prevent deposit formation in the tubes. P-1 is a small (10 to 15 hp) pump, operating *only* when the flow is low. The main cooling-tower pump (usually larger than 100 hp) is stopped when TCV-1A is closed.

Selection of optimum operating mode

The cost-effectiveness of heat recovery is a function of the outdoor temperature, the unit cost of energy from the alternative heat source, and the percentage of the

float 5° (say, from 40 to 45°F) before the chiller is restarted, this represents the equivalent of about 400 tons of thermal capacity. If the load happens to be 200 tons/h, the chiller can be turned off for 2 h at a time. If the load is 1,000 tons, the chiller will be off for only 24 minutes. The above illustrates the natural load-following time-proportioning nature of this scheme.

For longer rest periods

If the chiller needs a longer period of rest than the thermal capacity of the distribution system can provide, one has the option of:
1. Adding tankage to increase the water volume.
2. Starting up a second chiller, or distributing the load between chillers of different sizes by keeping some in continuous operation while cycling others. By continuously measuring the actual efficiency ($/ton) of each chiller, all loads can be met by the most efficient combination of machines for the load.

In plants with multiple refrigerant sources, the cost per ton of cooling can be calculated from direct measurements and used to establish the most efficient combination of units to meet present or anticipated loads. As with

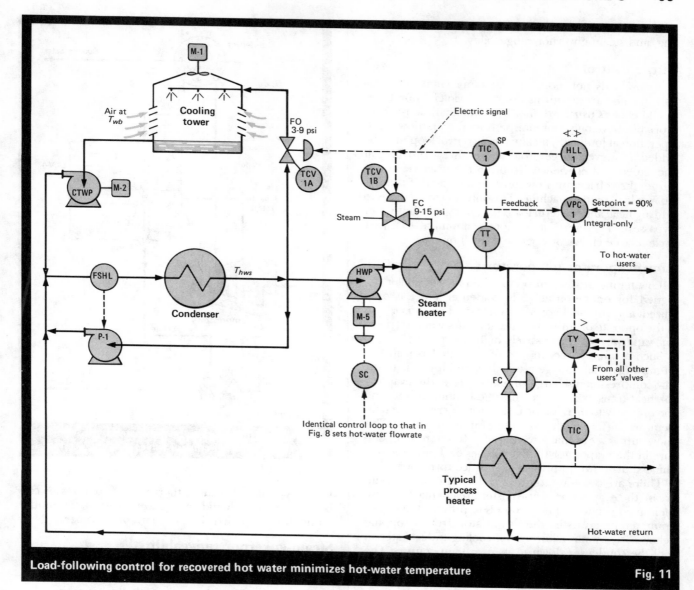

Load-following control for recovered hot water minimizes hot-water temperature   Fig. 11

cooling load that can be usefully employed as recovered heat. Calculations would show that if steam is available at $7/million Btu, and only half of the cooling load is needed as hot water, it is more economical to operate the chiller on cooling-tower water and use steam as the heat source when the outside air is below 65°F.

Conversely, when the outdoor temperature is above 75°F, the penalty for operating the split condenser at hot-water temperatures is no longer excessive; therefore, the plant should automatically switch back to recovered-heat operation. This cost-benefit analysis is a simple and continuously used part of the overall optimization scheme.

In such locations as the southern U.S. states, where there is no alternative heat source, such as a boiler or an outside steam line, another problem can arise because all the heating needs of the plant must be met by recovered heat from the heat pump. It is possible that on cold winter days there might not be enough recovered heat to meet this load. Whenever the heat load exceeds the cooling load and there is no other heat source available, an

artificial cooling load must be added to the heat pump.

This artificial heat source can, in some cases, be the cooling-tower water itself. A direct heat exchange between cooling-tower and chilled water streams is of advantage not only in this case, but also when there is no heat load—but when there is a small cooling load during the winter. At such times, the chiller can be stopped, and the small cooling load can be met by direct cooling from the cooling-tower water that is at a winter temperature.

Retrofitting chiller controls

In designing a plant, it is easy to specify variable-speed pumps, provide the thermal capacity required for chiller cycling, or locate chillers and cooling towers at the same elevation and near to each other so that the cooling-tower-water pumping costs will be minimized. In existing plants, the inherent design limitations must be accepted and the system optimized without any equipment changes. This is quite practical, and can still produce savings exceeding 50%, but precautions are needed.

In optimizing existing chillers, the constraints are

surge, low evaporator temperature, economizer flooding, and steam-governor rangeability.

Surge control

At low loads, not enough refrigerant is circulated. This can initiate surge, with its associated violent vibrations.

Old chillers usually do not have automatic surge controls, but have only vibration sensors for shutdown. For operation at low loads, an antisurge control loop must be added. However, surge protection is always provided at the expense of efficiency. To bring the machine out of surge, the refrigerant flow must be increased if there is no real load on the machine. The only way to do this is to add artificial and wasteful loads (i.e., hot-gas or hot-water bypasses). Therefore, it is more economical to either cycle a large chiller or operate a small one.

Low evaporator temperature

Low temperatures can occur when an old chiller designed for operation at 75°F condenser water is optimized, and run on 45 or 50°F water (in the winter). This is the opposite of surge, because it occurs when refrigerant vaporizes at an excessively high rate.

Such a situation occurs because the chiller is able to pump twice the tonnage it was designed for, due to the low compressor discharge pressure. Here, the evaporator heat-transfer area becomes the limiting factor, and the only way to increase heat flow is to increase the temperature differential across the evaporator tubes. This shows up as a gradual lowering of refrigerant temperature in the evaporator until it reaches 32°F, and the machine shuts down to protect against ice formation.

There are two ways to prevent this. The first is to increase the evaporator heat-transfer area (a major equipment modification). The second is to prevent the refrigerant temperature in the evaporator from dropping below 33°F, by not allowing the cooling-tower water to cool the condenser down to its own temperature. The latter solution requires adding a temperature-control loop that prevents the chiller from taking full advantage of the available cold water. The loop throttles the flow-rate, thereby causing a temperature rise.

Economizer flooding

On existing chillers, the economizer control valves, LCV-1 and LCV-2 in Fig. 12, are often sized on the basis that the refrigerant vapor pressure in the condenser, P_3, is constant and corresponds to a condenser water temperature of 75 or 85°F. When such units are operated with 45 or 50°F water, P_3 is reduced, and the pressure differentials across LCV-1 and LCV-2 are also less.

If this occurs—as it easily can—when the refrigerant circulation rate is high, the control valves will be unable to provide the necessary flowrate, and flooding of the economizer will occur (the flow is higher and the ΔP is lower than that used to size these valves.) The solution is to install larger valves, preferably external ones (located outside of the economizer) with two-mode control to eliminate offset. (Plain proportional controllers cannot maintain their setpoints as loads change, while the addition of the integral mode eliminates this offset.)

This is important in machines that were not originally designed for optimized, low-temperature condenser-

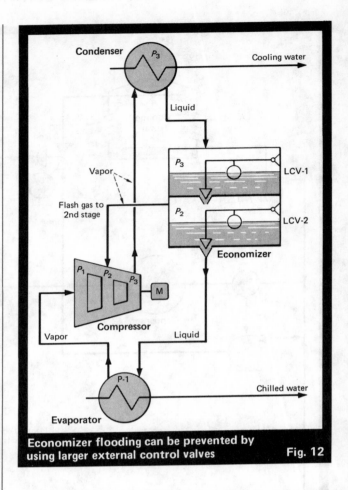

Economizer flooding can be prevented by using larger external control valves   Fig. 12

water operation, because otherwise the compressor can be damaged by liquid-refrigerant overflow from the economizer's flooded flash evaporator chamber.

Steam-governor rangeability

To optimize a steam-turbine-driven compressor, its rotational velocity must be modulated over a reasonably wide range. This is not possible with older machines, because they have quick-opening steam valves. A slight increase in lift from the fully closed position results in a substantial steam flow, and therefore a substantial rotational velocity. To try to throttle this steam flow makes the valve unstable and noisy. Valve characteristics can be changed from quick-opening. Wide rangeability can be obtained by welding two rings with V-notches to the seats of the existing steam-governor valves.

The author

Béla G. Lipták is president of Lipták Associates, 84 Old North Stamford Rd., Stamford, CT 06905. Tel: (203) 357-7614. He works as an instrumentation consultant on all phases of process-control projects. He received his degrees from The Technical University of Budapest, Stevens Institute of Technology, and The City College of New York. He has published about 75 technical articles and 11 books, the most recent of which is the revised edition of the "Instrument Engineers' Handbook on Process Measurement." He is a fellow of the Instrument Soc. of America and is a P.E. in several states.

Estimate air-cooler size

This program for the HP-41CV will help determine surface area, physical size and other parameters of air coolers.

Nadeem M. Shaikh, *S. H. Landes, Inc.*

☐ Often, at an early stage of a project, one must evaluate using air coolers, to see whether they can meet the cooling requirements of a process—and if they are feasible, to develop the cooler's capital investment cost, operating cost and the space requirements.

Several graphical techniques have been published for estimating air-cooler size. However, these methods do not provide any information about tubeside pressure drop, and analysis of horsepower versus surface and space requirements can be very laborious. The program presented in this article greatly reduces the calculation time and improves accuracy. Although written for the HP-41CV, it can be adapted for other programmable calculators. The main features of the program are:

■ It calculates the required extended surface, bay size, number and diameter of fans, driver horsepower, number of tubes, and tubeside velocity and pressure drop.

■ It makes calculations based upon the most commonly used 1-in. O.D., 14-BWG, ⅝ × 10, 2¼ in. △-pitch tube layout. The number of rows and corresponding extended area per square foot of bundle face area can be selected from Table III. This feature is quite helpful in analyzing the space requirement vs. horsepower. This is of particular interest in evaluating the air coolers for off-shore facilities. The greater the number of rows, the higher the horsepower required and the smaller the space.

■ It uses a curve-fit type of equation to correlate the air-side film coefficient and air static-pressure-drop across the bundle with the air mass-velocity for the selected tube layout [1]. This eliminates certain input data requirements such as fin thickness, spacing, height, conductivity, etc., for the estimation of air film coefficient.

■ It calculates the unit size within the allowable pressure drop.

■ It includes a provision for inputting the desired outlet-air temperature. This helps in analyzing the economics of increase in surface versus decrease in horsepower requirement. Higher outlet-air temperature would mean a lower air flowrate and, therefore, less horsepower required to drive the fans. At the same time, the *LMTD* and overall heat-transfer coefficient will decrease, thereby requiring more surface.

■ The program also makes it possible to input the tubeside film-coefficient, which will override the calculations for film resistance and pressure drop. This feature helps in estimating the size of condensers. For example, in the case of light-hydrocarbons condensing service, a tubeside film coefficient can be input as 450 Btu/ (h)(ft²)(°F) or, in the case of steam condensers, a film coefficient of 1,000 Btu/(h)(ft²)(°F) can be used. Calculations for two-phase pressure drop and heat-transfer rates are quite lengthy and involved, and no attempt has been made to cover them in this program.

■ It assumes the specific heat of air as 0.25 Btu/ (lb)(°F), for preliminary estimation. The program calculates the air density ratio based upon the average air-temperature across the bundle.

■ And the program enables one to study the effect of fouling on horsepower and surface requirements.

The basic philosophy of the calculation procedure is for one to select a particular unit configuration and then test it to see if it will work. The program input requirements are listed in Table IV.

As a starting point, an overall heat-transfer coefficient is assumed. The values of U_x given in Tables I and II can help in quick convergence. The air temperature rise is then estimated by the following equation [1]:

$$\Delta t_a = \left(\frac{U_x + 1}{10} \right)\left(\frac{T_1 + T_2}{2} - t_1 \right)$$

The outlet-air temperature thus arrived at is used to calculate the *LMTD*. A correlation factor of 1 is used, assuming that the unit will have three or more passes. The extended surface, A_x, is then calculated by the equation:

$$A_x = \frac{Q}{(U_x)(\Delta T_m)}$$

The bundle face area is determined by the appropriate APSF (area per square foot) factor given in Table III.

Approximate overall heat-transfer coefficients for air coolers that are cooling liquids	Table I

Material	Heat-transfer coefficient, U_x, Btu/(h)(ft²)(°F)
Water	6.1
Brine, 75% water	4.7
50% ethylene glycol-water	5.1
Ammonia	5.14
Hydrocarbon liquids, viscosity at average temperature, cP	
0.2	4.7
0.5	4.2
1.0	3.5
2.5	2.6
4.0	1.6
6.0	1.2
10.0	0.6

Originally published December 12, 1983

Heat-transfer coefficients for cooling by nitrogen were measured experimentally		Table I
Conditions	Material	Heat transfer coefficient, W/(m²)(K)
Cooling in liquid nitrogen	Steel	85–100
Cooling in a stream of nitrogen gas	Steel	5–10
Cooling in a stream of nitrogen gas	Rubber; polymers	20
Cooling by splashing liquid nitrogen	Steel	250–500

For nonconductive materials, thermal diffusivities are important in designing cooler		Table II
Material	Thermal diffusivity, m²/h	
Teflon	0.001	(100K)
Teflon	0.0005	(273K)
Rubber	0.00075	(200K)
Rubber	0.00055	(300K)
Polypropylene	0.0008	(140K)
Polypropylene	0.00035	(300K)
Polyethylene	0.0022	(140K)
Polyethylene	0.0006	(300K)
Polyvinyl chloride	0.0007	(140K)
Polyvinyl chloride	0.0004	(300K)

In the case of cryogenic cooling of rubber (for example, automobile scrap tires), the thermal diffusivity of the rubber is much lower than that of steel, so, as noted before, the thickness of the pieces to be cooled must be taken into account. The same general form of cooler is used, and design charts in terms of required residence time have been produced [10]. A typical example is shown in Fig. 2. The dependence of residence time on the maximum thickness of material is demonstrated, and the parameter here is the ratio of the specific area, A, to the bulk density, ρ_b, of the material. On the graph, points M and L represent typical values for medium-sized automobile tires and large truck tires.

We may use these design methods to evaluate the cooling-tunnel requirements for a tire treatment plant. Consider a plant designed to process 15 medium-sized automobile tires/min, which amounts to 5.6 million tires/yr [7]. For efficient use of the liquid nitrogen coolant, it is desirable to have a 10K temperature difference between entering rubber and exiting nitrogen gas at the warm end of the cooler. The required residence time in the precooling section from Fig. 3 is calculated at about 12 min, and the residence time in the final chilling section is about 3.6 min [10]. If the tires were not precut before cooling, the length of the required tunnel would be about 46 m; the consumption of liquid nitrogen would be near-ideal at 0.495 kg N_2/kg rubber; the liquid-nitrogen injection point would be about three-fourths of the way along the tunnel from the rubber inlet.

If we wished to reduce the length of the cooling tunnel, which naturally would require more nitrogen, we could design for a 50K warm-end temperature difference. This would result in a cooling tunnel 37 m long. The nitrogen consumption would have risen to 0.55 kg N_2/kg rubber. For an even shorter tunnel, the plant could be operated with a 100K warm-end difference, requiring a tunnel of 28m and calling for a nitrogen usage of 0.64 kg N_2/kg rubber. Design charts for the above conditions have been developed [10]. The liquid nitrogen usage for a well-designed plant would be about 100 metric tons/d.

Process economics

The economic viability of the process depends on the added value for a particular material. This added value is the difference between the price that can be obtained for the product and the cost of the scrap processed. In each instance, there will be a minimum added value needed for viability. The more the actual added value exceeds the minimum added value, the more profitable the process.

An economic analysis based on this principle was carried out in particular with reference to scrap automobile tires [11]. Details of this lengthy analysis will not be given here; however, it was shown that the cost of the nitrogen is by far the most important determinant in setting minimum added value. This emphasizes the need for good cooler design. The analysis was presented in the form of charts based on nitrogen cost. An example of such a chart is shown in Fig. 3, which includes materials in addition to rubber.

References

1. Bilbrey, J. H., Jr., "Use of Cryogenics in Scrap Processing," Proc. Fourth Mineral Waste Utilization Symposium, Chicago, May 1974.
2. Bilbrey, J. H. Jr., and Valdez, E. G., Use of Cryogenics in Scrap Processing, Adv. in Cryogenic Engineering, Vol. 20, 1975, p. 411.
3. Biddulph, M. W., Cryogenic Embrittlement of Some Polymers, Conservation and Recycling, Vol. 1, No. 3/4 1977, p. 281.
4. Anon., Freezing Scrap Cuts Materials Separation Costs, Processing, p. 13, Aug. 1975.
5. Valdez, E. G., Dean, K. C., and Wilson, W. J., "Use of Cryogens to Reclaim Non-Ferrous Scrap Metals," United States Bureau of Mines, Pub. No. RI 7716, 1973.
6. Braton, N. R., and Koutsky, J. A. Cryogenic Recycling, Proc. Fourth Mineral Waste Utilization Symposium, Chicago, May 1974.
7. Mishra, I. B., Koutsky, J. A., and Braton, N. R., Cryogenic Recycling of Solid Wastes, Polymer News, Vol. 2, No. 9/10, 1975, p. 32.
8. Wary, J., and Davies, R. B., Cryopulverising, Chemtech, March 1976, p. 200.
9. Biddulph, M. W., Cryogenic Embrittlement of Steel, Conservation and Recycling, Vol. 1, No. 2, 1977, p. 221.
10. Biddulph, M. W., Cryogenic Embrittlement of Rubber, Conservation and Recycling, Vol. 1, No. 2, 1977, p. 169.
11. Allen, D. H., and Biddulph, M. W., The Economic Evaluation of Cryopulverising, Conservation and Recycling, Vol. 2, No. 3/4, 1978, p. 255.
12. Freeguard, G. F., University of Nottingham, private communication.
13. Fredericks, S. L., "An Economic Evaluation of the Use of Cryogenics in Rubber Tire Reclaiming." Conf. Proc. Environ. Aspects of Chem. Use in Rubber Process Operations, Akron, Ohio, March 12-14, 1975, pp. 442-452.

The author

Michael W. Biddulph is a professor in the department of chemical engineering, University of Nottingham, University Park, Nottingham NG7 2RD, U.K. His research has been mainly in cryogenics, especially in recovering waste materials. He has been employed by British Oxygen Co. as a development engineer in low-temperature air separation, and has worked for Chevron Research Co. in the U.S., writing design programs. He holds bachelor's and Ph.D. degrees in chemical engineering from the University of Birmingham, and is a member of AIChE.

Designing a

Cooling water is expensive to circulate. Reducing its flow—i.e., hiking exchanger outlet temperatures—can cut tower, pump and piping investment as much as one-third and operating cost almost in half.

Ralph A. Crozier, Jr., E. I. du Pont de Nemours & Co.

☐ Heat-exchanger-network optimization has been accomplished in large integrated plants, such as petroleum refineries. In many of the chemical process industries, however, a plant contains several individual processes, and network optimization, except on a limited basis, is not feasible.

So far, no one has developed similar procedures for designing and optimizing a cooling-water once-through-exchanger system.* This article attempts to fill the void by presenting a design basis that will produce a "near optimum" system.

A cooling-water system consists of four major components: heat exchangers, cooling towers, circulation piping and pumps. To optimize such a system, one must define the system interactions and apply these relationships to the simultaneous design of the aforementioned

---

*The term "once-through cooling water" usually distinguishes river water from cooling-tower water. In this article, "cooling water once-through-exchanger system" means that the water passes through only one exchanger before it returns to the tower.

When a process is large, single-line and integrated, reducing cooling cost by circulating water through several exchangers in series before returning it to the tower is very attractive, especially if the coolant is used for refrigeration or turbine condensers. Such design, however, has very limited application in the typical multi-process, multi-step chemical plant, because parts of it may be shut down while other parts are still operated.

equipment. This article develops criteria that for most applications allow one to ignore system interactions, and still design a "near optimum" system.

Cooling-water systems have long been designed by "rules of thumb" that call for fixing the coolant temperature-rise across all heat exchangers (usually 20°F) and setting the coolant inlet temperature to the heat exchanger at the site's wet-bulb temperature plus 8°F. These rules produce a workable cooling system; but, by taking the same coolant rise across all exchangers, regardless of the individual process outlet-temperatures, this cannot result in an optimized design.

The design method presented in this article replaces the "rules of thumb" with criteria that are easy to apply and that take into account the effect that the individual exchanger process outlet-temperatures have on cooling-system economics.

Economic analyses of actual processes have shown that cooling-system investment can be reduced by one third, and cooling-system operating cost by one half, if the proposed design criteria are used instead of the "rules of thumb." It has been found that the controlling economic factor for a cooling system is the quantity of

Originally published April 21, 1980

"near optimum" cooling-water system

water being circulated. Reducing the flow (raising the coolant outlet temperature of heat exchangers) significantly reduces cooling-tower, pump and piping investment, and operating cost, and only moderately increases the heat-exchanger investment. The overriding conclusion to be drawn is that cooling water is very expensive, and its conservation can result in significant savings.

Three system interactions

What are the system interactions and their relationships? When can they be ignored, and when must they be considered?

From Fig. 1, it can be seen that there are three coolant interactions: (1) between the outlet temperature of the heat exchanger and the inlet temperature of the cooling tower, (2) between the inlet temperature of the exchanger and the outlet temperature of the cooling tower, and (3) between total coolant flowrate and the size of connecting piping and circulating pumps.

First Interaction—In the Fig. 1 system, cooling water enters the shell side of the exchanger at a fixed temperature of T_1 and exits at a variable temperature of T_2; the process fluid passes through the tube side at fixed inlet and outlet temperatures of t_1 and t_2, respectively. The cooling tower dissipates heat to the ambient air through humidification (evaporation) and sensible heating.

Cooling-tower investment and operating cost are reduced by returning the water to the tower as hot as possible, because the hotter the water, the larger the temperature difference (thermal driving force) between it and the ambient air; hence, less heat-transfer area (tower packing) is required. Additionally, as the effluent air temperature is raised, so is the moisture content of the exiting air; hence, less air flow is necessary.

Upping the temperature of the water to the tower also cuts down the quantity of water circulated through the tower. From Eq. (1), it can be seen that for a fixed heat load and tower outlet temperature (T_{out}), the quantity of cooling water required to satisfy the heat balance is inversely proportional to the tower inlet temperature (T_{in}):

$$W_T = Q_T/[C(T_{in} - T_{out})] \qquad (1)$$

Boosting the tower inlet temperature means increasing the coolant temperature rise across the individual exchangers; hence, to reduce cooling-tower investment and operating cost, one must widen the coolant temperature rise across the individual exchangers.

A significant discovery has been that in most instances exchanger area is relatively insensitive to incre-

mental changes in coolant outlet temperature. To understand this, one must recognize that a well designed exchanger must have adequate heat-transfer area, but it must also have sufficient fluid-flow area to satisfy the shell-and-tube pressure-drop restrictions.

Because coolant flowrate is inversely proportional to coolant temperature rise, a small coolant temperature rise produces a large increase in coolant flow. This means that the exchanger diameter must be increased, if the pressure-drop (maximum velocity) restriction is to be satisfied.

If the heat-transfer equation $Q = UA(LMTD)$ were solved for the small coolant temperature-rise geometry, it would show that the area needed for heat transfer is less than required by the pressure-drop limitation. In other words, for small coolant temperature rises, the exchanger's heat-transfer area would be excessive if determined by fluid-flow considerations.

If the coolant outlet temperature is sequentially increased and the required exchanger area is calculated for the different coolant temperature rises, a plot similar to that in Fig. 2 would be generated. Notice that the required exchanger area initially lessens, reaches a maximum, and then gains as the coolant temperature rise is increased.

The required exchanger area, as depicted in Fig. 2, passes through three distinct design regions. In the first (80°F to 115°F), the required area is controlled by fluid-flow phenomena. In the second (115°F to 158°F), the fluid-flow and heat transfer considerations are the same order of magnitude; that is, neither requirement is controlling. In the third (above 158°F), the heat-transfer requirement becomes controlling (reduced $LMTD$). Therefore, to minimize exchanger area, the design should be in the second (transition) region.

Fig. 2 was developed on the basis of full tube bundle. At low coolant temperatures, the better design would be to have the tube bundle partially filled, so as to maintain a constant tubeside velocity. In the transition region, however, the shell velocity was kept at a constant rate by reducing the baffle spacing as the coolant flow decreased.

Second Interaction—The tower outlet temperature (approach plus wet bulb) is the variable with which the cooling-tower designer has the least latitude, yet it is the most significant determinant of cooling-tower investment and operating cost. The tower outlet temperature is the "Achilles heel" of this study and the reason why only a "near optimum," rather than a truly optimized, cooling system is attained.

Specifying the coolant outlet temperature is difficult

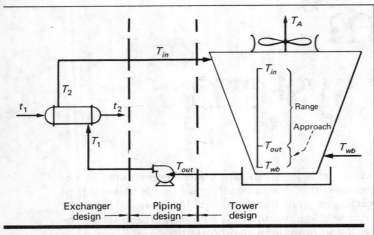

Typical system demonstrates three interactions   Fig. 1

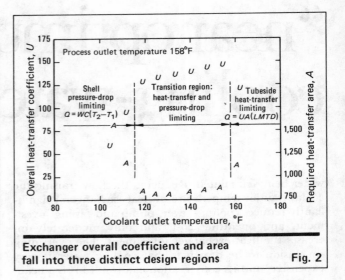

Exchanger overall coefficient and area fall into three distinct design regions   Fig. 2

because it is bound on the lower side by the wet-bulb temperature and on the upper side by the minimum process outlet temperature. To minimize cooling-tower investment and operating cost, one needs to maximize the approach to wet-bulb temperature. However, to minimize heat-exchanger investment, one needs to maximize the approach to the minimum process outlet temperature. Therefore, the tower outlet temperature has to be a compromise between these two boundaries.

The importance of the cooling-tower and heat-exchanger designers' discussing the temperature limitations imposed on each before any calculations are started cannot be overemphasized. Usually, the lowest cooling temperature is required for a refrigeration system or a steam turbine condenser. Considerable savings can be realized if alternative cooling methods are provided for these services, rather than penalizing the entire cooling system for one, or both, of them.

Many cooling towers are designed by a rule of thumb that sets the tower outlet temperature equal to the site wet-bulb temperature plus 8°F. This can result in significant cooling-tower investment and operating cost penalties if process requirements do not demand cooling water at a temperature that low. As previously stated, cooling-tower investment and operating cost are minimized by maximizing the approach to wet-bulb temperature.

Third Interaction—Via Eq. (1), it can be shown that the system flowrate decreases as the tower inlet temperature is hiked. Therefore, as the coolant rise across the individual exchangers is increased, the supply and return piping, as well as the circulating pumps, can be reduced in size.

In summary, the investment and operating cost of the tower, pumps and piping will be reduced when the cooling-tower inlet temperature is increased. The exchanger investment may or may not be reduced as the coolant temperature rise is increased, depending on the relationship of the coolant outlet temperature and the exchanger design region (Fig. 2).

If the exchanger's optimum coolant outlet temperature is in the transition region, its area will be minimized, and system interactions can be ignored. If the

exchanger's coolant outlet temperature is not in the transition region, however, system interactions must be considered.

It has been empirically determined that if the exchanger *LMTD* is greater than 30°F when the coolant outlet temperature is set at the process outlet temperature or some maximum temperature (scaling limitation), the exchanger is in the transition region. If the *LMTD* is less than 30°F, the exchanger is in the heat-transfer-limiting region and the exchanger area will be very sensitive to coolant temperature changes. Therefore, if the *LMTD* is less than 30°F, system interactions must be considered; and a compromise between higher exchanger investment and lower cooling-tower investment must be determined.

Constraints on outlet temperature

Two temperature constraints limit the exchanger coolant outlet temperature. First, the wood fill of the conventionally designed cooling tower limits the maximum water temperature to 150°F. Second, the temperature from individual exchangers is set by process outlet temperatures or by tube fouling or material of construction.

Waterside deposits of suspended solids, mineral salts, biological growths, and corrosion products interfere with heat transfer. In the design calculations for sizing heat exchangers, the magnitude of the interference is the fouling factor. Attempts to quantitatively relate the factor to specific fouling conditions have been only partially successful; therefore, the numerical value assigned to different degrees of fouling by specific deposits has been based largely on experience.

Because there is no theoretical basis for selecting fouling factors at different coolant temperatures, the same factor was used at all temperatures in this study. To analyze the effect of this assumption on the conclusions, a cooling system for which the fouling factor was arbitrarily doubled was evaluated. It was found that the cooling tower, pump and piping investment and operating cost savings far outweighed the higher exchanger investment and operating cost. Therefore, the conclusions reached in the increased-fouling-factor evaluation

Choosing economic insulation thickness

Optimum insulation thickness depends on the designer's selection of factors for balancing economic and engineering criteria. Here are some guidelines being used by experts in the field.

Alan R. Koenig, Jim Walter Research Corp.

☐ What is the most economic thickness of insulation? Unfortunately, there is no single answer to this question, as an almost infinite number of physical, mechanical and economic variables are involved. However, with rapidly escalating energy costs, getting a good answer is becoming more important.

Equations for estimating heat loss

There are a number of methods for estimating the theoretical heat loss through insulation. A particularly useful one is the graphical solution, which allows the designer to gauge the relative effects of several variables.

The three modes of heat transfer include losses by conduction through the insulation, radiation losses to the air, and convection losses caused by the movement of the air. Because the heat lost through the insulation must equal that transferred to the surroundings:

$$Q \text{ Conduction} = Q \text{ Radiation} + Q \text{ Convection} \quad (1)$$

In the graphical solution, various values for the surface temperature of the insulation are assumed, and heat loss at the chosen temperatures is determined. The intersection of (a) the curves of the heat loss by conduction and (b) the heat losses by radiation plus convection represents the surface temperature and heat loss condition set that satisfies Eq. (1).

The heat loss by conduction is a function of the thermal conductivity and thickness of the insulation components.

For a flat surface:

$$Q_{cd} = (T_h - T_s)/[(l_1/k_1) + (l_2/k_2)] + \cdots \quad (2)$$

For pipe:

$$Q_{cd} = \frac{T_h - T_s}{[r_3 \ln(r_2/r_1)/k_1] + [r_3 \ln(r_3/r_2)/k_2]} + \cdots \quad (3)$$

When the insulation is homogeneous, the denominators in Eq. (2) and (3) reduce to a single term because the thermal conductivity is uniform.

The heat lost to the air by radiation is given by:

$$Q_r = 0.1713\varepsilon\left[\left(\frac{T_s + 459.6}{100}\right)^4 - \left(\frac{T_a + 459.6}{100}\right)^4\right] \quad (4)$$

The heat loss by convection is a function of the temperature difference between the insulation surface and the air, and the speed at which the air passes over the surface [1]:

$$Q_{cv} = C\left(\frac{1}{d}\right)^{0.2}\left(\frac{1}{T_{av}}\right)^{0.181}(\Delta T)^{1.266}(1 + 1.277v)^{1/2} \quad (5)$$

Originally published September 8, 1980

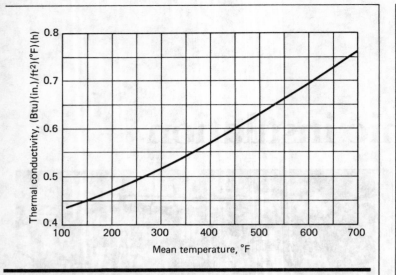

Perlitic insulation curve can be considered linear   Fig. 1

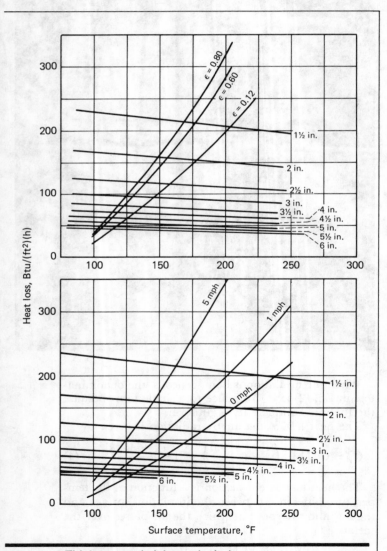

**Thickness, emissivity and wind
factors affect insulation heat loss   Fig. 2**

Here, C is a constant that depends on the shape of the surface. Values of this constant are: 1.016 for horizontal cylinders, 1.235 for long vertical cylinders, 1.394 for vertical plates, 1.79 for horizontal plates facing up, and 0.89 for horizontal plates facing down.

Somewhat simpler but less exact is Langmuir's equation:

$$Q_{cv} = 0.296(T_s - T_a)^{5/4}(1 + 1.277v)^{1/2} \qquad (6)$$

Example of graphical method

The graphical solution is best explained by an example. The design data are: iron pipe size—8.00 in.; operating temperature—800°F; average ambient air temperature—80°F; wind velocity—1 mph; insulation—Celotemp 1500; jacketings—aluminum, white paint, stainless steel; and emissivities—for bare pipe, 0.80; aluminum jacketing, 0.12; white painted canvas, 0.60; stainless steel, 0.80.

The thermal conductivity curve for a perlitic high-temperature insulation is given in Fig. 1. Values for thermal conductivity vs. mean temperature follow a second-order equation; however, over a relatively small (100°F) temperature range, the curve can be considered linear. Therefore, two points can define the line when the heat loss through a particular thickness of this insulation is being determined. Inside and outside diameters of pipe insulation are given in ASTM C-585, "Inner and Outer Diameters of Rigid Thermal Insulation for Nominal Sizes of Pipe and Tubing" [2].

For an insulation O.D. of 15 in. and I.D. of 8.7 in., and an insulation thermal conductivity of 0.58 (Btu) (in.)/(ft²)(°F)(h) (from Fig. 1, at a mean temperature of 450°F), the heat loss by conduction through 3-in.-thick perlitic pipe insulation covering an 8-in.-dia. pipe at a surface temperature of 100°F would be 99 Btu/(ft²)(h), calculated via Eq. (3).

Similarly, heat losses by conduction for other insulation thicknesses are plotted in Fig. 2.

The next step is to calculate the heat losses stemming from radiation and convection. A separate curve is required for each jacketing material. Generally, three points can adequately define such a curve.

If $T_s = 100°F$, $\varepsilon = 0.12$, and $T_a = 80°F$, then $Q_r = 3$ Btu/(ft²)(h), via Eq. (4).

Via Eq. (6), with $v = 1$ mph, $Q_{cv} = 19$ Btu/(ft²)(h). Therefore, $Q_r + Q_{cv} = 22$ Btu/(ft²)(h).

Heat losses for surface temperatures of 150°F and 200°F, and for emissivities of 0.60 and 0.80, are also calculated, and the results plotted in Fig. 2. The intersections between the conductive and the radiant-plus-convective loss curves represent the theoretical heat losses for the system at various surface temperatures.

The velocity of air passing over insulation will significantly affect heat loss. Also plotted in Fig. 2 are heat losses calculated via Eq. (6) at wind velocities of 0, 1 and 5 mph, with insulation having a surface emissivity of $\varepsilon = 0.12$.

Other causes of heat loss

System designers agree that a design margin has to be added to theoretically calculated values of heat loss and

Nomenclature

C	Constant that depends on shape of the surface used in calculating heat transfer by convection
d	Diameter of outermost layer of pipe insulation system, in.
i_1	Annual projected fuel inflation rate, decimal
i_2	Current interest rate, decimal
k	Thermal conductivity of an insulation layer at a particular mean temperature, $(Btu)(in.)/(ft^2)(°F)(h)$
l	Thickness of an insulation layer, in.
n	Time period, yr
P	Positive cash flow, $/ft
Q_{cd}	Heat transfer by conduction, $Btu/(ft^2)(h)$
Q_r	Heat transfer by radiation, $Btu/(ft^2)(h)$
Q_{cv}	Heat transfer by convection, $Btu/(ft^2)(h)$
r_1	Radius of innermost layer of pipe insulation system, in.
r_2	Radius of an intermediate layer of pipe insulation system composed of more than one type of insulation, in.
r_3	Radius of outermost layer of pipe insulation system, in.
S	Incremental insulation investment, $/ft
T_a	Surrounding air temperature, °F
T_{av}	Average temperature of insulation surface and surrounding air, °F
T_h	Hot-face temperature of insulation, °F
T_s	Cold-face temperature of insulation, °F
ΔT	Difference between surface temperature and surrounding air temperature, °F
v	Surrounding air velocity, mph
ε	Surface emissivity of outermost layer of insulation system

surface temperatures to account for workmanship, thermal expansion, intrusions into the insulation and possible loss of performance with time. The magnitude of this factor will depend on personal judgment based on experience, and has been known to range from 25 to 300%.

Small openings in insulation can allow significant heat loss. Such openings occur at joints between insulation half-sections, around valves and flanges, at gouges and breaks in insulation, and are also caused by differences in thermal expansion between pipe and insulation.

In the example system, a gap as small as $\frac{1}{16}$ in. between adjacent sections of insulation can cause a heat loss of up to 37 Btu/(ft)(h). And heat losses from the seam between half-sections of insulation with a closure gap of $\frac{1}{16}$ in. could be as large as 99 Btu/(ft)(h).

When heated, metal pipes expand more than insulation does. Also, when first heated, all high-temperature insulation tends to shrink. This opposing expansion and contraction can cause fissure cracks. In the sample problem, these cracks theoretically could allow as much as 200–300 Btu/(ft)(h) from an insulated carbon steel pipe. Generally, the magnitude of this loss will be much smaller because the cracks will rarely extend completely through the insulation.

Moisture in insulation will also hike heat losses, and water is present in almost all thermal insulation. It is difficult to accurately estimate the heat loss that can be attributed to moisture. The loss will depend not only on the insulation's water content but also on its porosity, the temperature profile through it, and the type and condition of the jacketing. One rule of thumb states: A 1% increase in moisture content will boost thermal conductivity by 5%.

Economics of insulation thickness

In some cases, technical and safety considerations will primarily determine the insulation thickness. Most often, however, economic criteria will prevail. Insula-

tion investment is judged in most companies by economic criteria via a fixed accounting method, which can significantly affect the choice of insulation thickness. Some of the more common methods include simple payback, minimum annual cost, and maximum present value of cash flow.

Simple payback—In its simplest form, this method compares the savings from reduced heat loss to the cost of the insulation system—with the return determined in months or years. The common criterion for the payback period is from one to three years.

Table I presents heat-loss data calculated for the sample pipe-insulation system, having aluminum jacketing—with a wind speed of 1 mph. Process heat is assumed to cost $3.06 per million Btu, based on oil at $20/bbl (heating value taken as 140,000 Btu/gal), and 90% conversion efficiency.

Heat losses were obtained from Fig. 2. These values were increased by dividing them by a design factor of 0.75, to account for the additional heat losses discussed. Finally, the heat losses per hour were converted to an annual basis, assuming an operating time of 6,000 h/yr.

Estimated installed costs of the insulation systems, in $\frac{1}{2}$-in. increments, are given in Table II. The 1.15 piping complexity factor represents average installation.

The additional cost for incremental insulation thickness is divided by incremental cost savings to obtain the Table I payback periods. If the payback criterion selected were two years, an insulation thickness of 3 in. would be chosen.

With fuel costs increasing rapidly, some estimators choose to increase the current cost of fuel in the simple payback calculation by an escalation factor. This is commonly done by assuming a linear annual-percentage increase in fuel costs, and using this percentage in the calculation of the escalator factor:

$$\text{Fuel-cost escalator} = \frac{(1 + i_1)^n - 1}{i_1 n} \qquad (7)$$

Simple payback at an assumed heat cost of $3.06/million Btu — Table I

Insulation thickness, in.	Annual cost heat loss, $/(ft)(yr)	Annual heat savings, $/(ft)(yr)	Cost of insulation, $/ft	Incremental cost, $/ft	Payback, yr
0	193.51	–	–	–	–
1½	15.12	178.39	7.08	7.08	0.04
2	12.18	2.94	8.98	1.91	0.94
2½	10.10	2.08	10.94	1.96	0.94
3	8.84	1.26	12.32	1.38	1.10
3½	7.31	1.53	16.36	4.04	2.64
4	6.82	0.49	18.81	2.45	5.00
4½	6.30	0.52	21.52	2.71	5.21
5	5.91	0.39	23.79	2.27	5.82
5½	5.66	0.25	26.05	2.26	9.04
6	5.36	0.30	28.90	2.85	9.50

Estimated total installed costs of the sample insulation — Table II

Insulation thickness, in.	Costs, $/ft				
	Insulation	Jacketing*	Installation	Total	With complexity factor of 1.15
1½	2.95	0.61	2.60	6.16	7.08
2	4.15	0.66	3.00	7.81	8.98
2½	5.38	0.73	3.40	9.51	10.94
3	6.13	0.78	3.80	10.71	12.32
3½	8.39	0.84	5.00	14.23	16.36
4	9.87	0.89	5.60	16.36	18.81
4½	11.57	0.94	6.20	18.71	21.52
5	12.89	1.00	6.80	20.69	23.79
5½	14.21	1.04	7.40	22.65	26.05
6	16.03	1.10	8.00	25.13	28.90

*Based on $0.20/ft²
†Piping complexity factor accounts for extra costs associated with covering elbows, valves, etc. In practice, this factor can range from 1.0 to 1.6, depending on the complexity of installation and size of the line.

Assuming an annual fuel-cost rise of 10%/yr for 10 years, the average cost of the sample fuel would be $4.88/million Btu. On this basis, a two-year payback would call for an insulation thickness of 3.5 in.

Minimum annual cost—In this accounting method, all costs are annualized, then discounted at an assigned interest rate. The insulation chosen is that which yields the minimum annual cost:

$$\text{System cost} = \text{insulation cost} + \text{energy cost} \quad (8)$$

Insulation cost commonly includes installed cost and cost of maintenance (usually a percentage of initial insulation cost). Costs normally associated with energy include the initial cost of the equipment for producing the desired form of energy, the maintenance cost of this equipment, and direct costs for the fuel, with escalations

for inflation. Depreciation on equipment and insulation costs is usually also taken into account.

To annualize the cost of the insulation, its initial cost is multiplied by a capital recovery factor:

$$\text{CRF} = \frac{i_2(1 + i_2)^n}{(1 + i_2)^n - 1} \quad (9)$$

The cost of the heating equipment is obtained by multiplying the heat loss per linear foot, the cost of the equipment to produce the heat, and the capital recovery factor. The maintenance cost of the heating equipment is determined by multiplying the heat loss per linear foot times the cost of the equipment to produce the heat times the yearly maintenance cost percentage of the equipment. The cost of heat = annual heat loss × first-year cost of heat × 1 − (tax rate/100) × Discount Factor (DF).

$$\text{DF} = (\text{CRF}) \sum_{n-1}^{n} \frac{(1 + i_1)^{n-1}}{(1 + i_2)^n} \quad (10)$$

If the fuel inflation rate equals the interest rate, Eq. (10) reduces to:

$$\text{DF} = (\text{CRF})n/(1 + i_2) \quad (11)$$

The tax saving is computed by multiplying, by the tax rate, the investment costs for the insulation and the heat-generating equipment, and dividing the product by the expected life of the equipment.

The total annual cost for the installation is the sum of the original cost of the insulation and its maintenance cost, the cost of the heating equipment and its maintenance cost, and the cost of the heat—less the tax saving.

Discounted payback—This is the time required for a capital investment to generate discounted, after-tax cash flows equal to the initial investment. The investment payback in years is calculated with Eq. (12):

$$n = \frac{\ln P/[(P - Si_2)}{\ln(1 + i_2)} \quad (12)$$

Using this method, the economic thickness of the insulation for the sample problem would generally be 3½ in.

References

1. Heilman, R. H., "Surface Heat Transmission," Trans. Am. Soc. Mech. Engrs., Vol. 51, 1929, p. 257.
2. "Annual Book of ASTM Standards, Part 18," American Soc. for Testing and Materials, Philadelphia, 1979.

The author

Alan R. Koenig is head of a research section at Jim Walter Research Corp. (10301 Ninth St. North, St. Petersburg, FL 33702). He has been with the Celotex Industrial Products Div. for 13 years. Previously, he had been with General Electric Corp. and Gulf Oil Corp. Active in the ASTM C-16 (thermal insulation) committee, he is a member of Keramos, honorary ceramic engineering society, and Sigma Xi, honorary engineering society. He holds B.S. and M.S. degrees in ceramic engineering from Georgia Institute of Technology.

Preventing burns from insulated pipes

Personnel safety depends not only on pipe insulation thickness, but on the insulation jacket. The difference between a shiny and a dull jacket-surface can mean the difference between a serious burn and mild discomfort.

M. McChesney and *P. McChesney, Fuel Save Associates*

☐ Recently the writers were asked to advise on the insulation of steam headers—the main steam line into which boilers are connected—to ensure that the insulation was not only economic but also safe. Because of the very high steam-temperatures involved, together with the new tough laws on health and safety at work, it was imperative that there should be no risk of skin burns to those who came into contact with the insulated headers.

Steam headers are usually large-diameter pipes (up to 30-in. dia.) and in this particular case we were asked to consider both 10- and 20-in. pipes. Their insulation is essential not only to conserve heat but also to avoid high boiler base-loads, which increase the fuel bill out of all proportion to their size.

Insulation guidelines

There are general guidelines for header insulation laid down by various organizations. In the U.S., those given by NIMA (National Insulation Manufacturers Assn.) are typical [1]. Specifically, large-diameter hot pipes should be insulated with curved preformed sections, which should have an outer covering to ensure, among other reasons, that the insulation is neither damaged nor crushed and that it is fully protected from the weather.

This outer finish depends upon where the pipes are. For example, if they are indoors, the finish can be light-weight canvas; but if outdoors, the finish must be completely waterproof. This is obvious, and yet what is not often realized is that once wet, insulation may never become dry. Even a steam header at 1,000°F may have wet insulation because some of the insulation will be below 212°F; the heat transfer through the insulation will only completely dry it as far as the 212° isotherm, leaving the outermost insulation still damp. Insulation containing water is only about a tenth as effective as the same insulation when completely dry.

Although both weather-barrier mastic and aluminum (or perhaps even stainless steel) jacketing are used for outdoor weather protection, the metal jacketing is to be preferred since there is a chance it will allow water vapor to escape outwards.

A common header insulant is calcium silicate: it has high compressive and flexural strength, it meets the specifications for prevention of stress-corrosion cracking of austenitic stainless steels and, being a mixture of lime and silica reinforced with fibers, it can readily be moulded into preformed sections. Weather protection of calcium silicate is essential since not only can it hold about 70% of its own weight of water without losing rigidity, but it has the astonishing capability of being able to hold about 350% of its own weight of water without actually dripping (showing that it is wet)!

Before attempting to calculate the economic thickness of insulation—and this proved to be a vexing problem for reasons we shall give in a later article—the writers considered the following problems: 1. What is the

Originally published July 27, 1981

(Continued) Table VI

Step	Code	Key	Step	Code	Key	Step	Code	Key	Step	Code	Key	Step	Code	Key
027	43	RCL	091	52	EE	155	43	RCL	219	43	RCL	283	24	24
028	01	01	092	99	PRT	156	01	01	220	11	11	284	61	GTO
029	32	X:T	093	76	LBL	157	75	-	221	65	×	285	12	B
030	43	RCL	094	12	B	158	43	RCL	222	43	RCL	286	76	LBL
031	03	03	095	02	2	159	02	02	223	10	10	287	32	X:T
032	67	EQ	096	65	×	160	95	=	224	95	=	288	22	INV
033	95	=	097	53	(	161	22	INV	225	42	STO	289	86	STF
034	77	GE	098	43	RCL	162	87	IFF	226	53	53	290	00	00
035	22	INV	099	01	01	163	00	00	227	44	SUM	291	22	INV
036	76	LBL	100	75	-	164	33	X²	228	02	02	292	52	EE
037	95	=	101	43	RCL	165	94	+/-	229	43	RCL	293	98	ADV
038	22	INV	102	02	02	166	76	LBL	230	02	02	294	43	RCL
039	87	IFF	103	54	)	167	33	X²	231	99	PRT	295	02	02
040	00	00	104	65	×	168	45	YX	232	43	RCL	296	99	PRT
041	85	+	105	89	π	169	43	RCL	233	02	02	297	43	RCL
042	76	LBL	106	65	×	170	24	24	234	75	-	298	07	07
043	22	INV	107	43	RCL	171	95	=	235	43	RCL	299	99	PRT
044	86	STF	108	00	00	172	42	STO	236	03	03	300	91	R/S
045	00	00	109	55	÷	173	56	56	237	95	=	301	76	LBL
046	43	RCL	110	53	(	174	22	INV	238	42	STO	302	13	C
047	03	03	111	53	(	175	87	IFF	239	52	52	303	22	INV
048	75	-	112	43	RCL	176	00	00	240	22	INV	304	87	IFF
049	53	(	113	05	05	177	34	ГX	241	87	IFF	305	02	02
050	53	(	114	55	÷	178	94	+/-	242	00	00	306	44	SUM
051	43	RCL	115	43	RCL	179	42	STO	243	35	1/X	307	71	SBR
052	03	03	116	04	04	180	56	56	244	94	+/-	308	45	YX
053	75	-	117	54	)	181	76	LBL	245	42	STO	309	76	LBL
054	43	RCL	118	23	LNX	182	34	ГX	246	52	52	310	44	SUM
055	01	01	119	54	)	183	43	RCL	247	76	LBL	311	43	RCL
056	54	)	120	95	=	184	20	20	248	35	1/X	312	02	02
057	45	YX	121	42	STO	185	55	÷	249	00	0	313	75	-
058	93	.	122	07	07	186	43	RCL	250	32	X:T	314	43	RCL
059	05	5	123	22	INV	187	07	07	251	43	RCL	315	03	03
060	05	5	124	87	IFF	188	65	×	252	52	52	316	95	=
061	54	)	125	00	00	189	53	(	253	67	EQ	317	22	INV
062	95	=	126	25	CLR	190	43	RCL	254	42	STO	318	87	IFF
063	42	STO	127	50	IxI	191	04	04	255	77	GE	319	00	00
064	02	02	128	42	STO	192	45	YX	256	12	B	320	52	EE
065	61	GTO	129	07	07	193	43	RCL	257	76	LBL	321	94	+/-
066	23	LNX	130	76	LBL	194	24	24	258	42	STO	322	76	LBL
067	76	LBL	131	25	CLR	195	54	)	259	01	1	323	52	EE
068	85	+	132	71	SBR	196	55	÷	260	85	+	324	65	×
069	43	RCL	133	13	C	197	43	RCL	261	43	RCL	325	01	1
070	03	03	134	43	RCL	198	05	05	262	03	03	326	02	2
071	85	+	135	07	07	199	65	×	263	95	=	327	55	÷
072	53	(	136	75	-	200	43	RCL	264	42	STO	328	43	RCL
073	53	(	137	43	RCL	201	56	56	265	02	02	329	05	05
074	43	RCL	138	58	58	202	95	=	266	87	IFF	330	95	=
075	01	01	139	95	=	203	42	STO	267	00	00	331	45	YX
076	75	-	140	42	STO	204	55	55	268	43	RCL	332	93	.
077	43	RCL	141	20	20	205	43	RCL	269	43	RCL	333	02	2
078	03	03	142	50	IxI	206	10	10	270	03	03	334	05	5
079	54	)	143	32	X:T	207	42	STO	271	75	-	335	95	=
080	45	YX	144	43	RCL	208	54	54	272	01	1	336	22	INV
081	93	.	145	07	07	209	43	RCL	273	95	=	337	87	IFF
082	05	5	146	65	×	210	55	55	274	42	STO	338	00	00
083	05	5	147	93	.	211	42	STO	275	02	02	339	53	(
084	54	)	148	00	0	212	10	10	276	76	LBL	340	94	+/-
085	95	=	149	00	0	213	55	÷	277	43	RCL	341	76	LBL
086	42	STO	150	01	1	214	43	RCL	278	99	PRT	342	53	(
087	02	02	151	95	=	215	54	54	279	93	.	343	65	×
088	76	LBL	152	50	IxI	216	95	=	280	01	1	344	93	.
089	23	LNX	153	77	GE	217	44	SUM	281	22	INV	345	02	2
090	22	INV	154	32	X:T	218	11	11	282	44	SUM	346	07	7

(Continued) Table VI

Step	Code	Key	Step	Code	Key	Step	Code	Key	Step	Code	Key	Step	Code	Key
347	65	×	373	61	GTO	399	42	STO	425	04	4	451	43	RCL
348	43	RCL	374	42	STO	400	43	43	426	06	6	452	04	04
349	59	59	375	46	46	401	22	INV	427	00	0	453	48	EXC
350	65	×	376	43	RCL	402	87	IFF	428	54	)	454	05	05
351	53	(	377	03	03	403	00	00	429	55	÷	455	42	STO
352	43	RCL	378	42	STO	404	15	E	430	01	1	456	04	04
353	02	02	379	47	47	405	50	I×I	431	00	0	457	43	RCL
354	75	-	380	71	SBR	406	76	LBL	432	00	0	458	21	21
355	43	RCL	381	61	GTO	407	15	E	433	54	)	459	48	EXC
356	03	03	382	94	+/-	408	85	+	434	45	Y×	460	22	22
357	54	)	383	85	+	409	43	RCL	435	04	4	461	42	STO
358	95	=	384	43	RCL	410	08	08	436	95	=	462	21	21
359	22	INV	385	46	46	411	95	=	437	42	STO	463	92	RTN
360	87	IFF	386	95	=	412	42	STO	438	45	45	464	76	LBL
361	00	00	387	65	×	413	58	58	439	92	RTN	465	10	E'
362	71	SBR	388	43	RCL	414	87	IFF	440	76	LBL	466	43	RCL
363	50	I×I	389	22	22	415	01	01	441	45	Y×	467	43	43
364	76	LBL	390	65	×	416	10	E'	442	22	INV	468	42	STO
365	71	SBR	391	43	RCL	417	92	RTN	443	86	STF	469	06	06
366	42	STO	392	59	59	418	76	LBL	444	02	02	470	71	SBR
367	08	08	393	65	×	419	61	GTO	445	43	RCL	471	45	Y×
368	43	RCL	394	93	.	420	53	(	446	01	01	472	22	INV
369	02	02	395	01	1	421	53	(	447	48	EXC	473	86	STF
370	42	STO	396	07	7	422	43	RCL	448	02	02	474	01	01
371	47	47	397	03	3	423	47	47	449	42	STO	475	61	GTO
372	71	SBR	398	95	=	424	85	+	450	01	01	476	13	C

User instructions and example for TI version

Table VII

Step	Instruction	Input data	Example	Key	Output
1.	Enter program by key or card				
2.	Store input data:				
	Thermal conductivity, Btu/(h)(ft^2)(°F)(ft)	K_m	0.028	STO 00	
	Temperature inside pipe, °F	T_1	366	STO 01	
	Temperature of air, °F	T_3	80	STO 03	
	Diameter of pipe, in.	D_1	3.5	STO 04	
	Diameter of insulation, in.	D_2	5.5	STO 05	
	Emissivity of pipe	e_p	0.79	STO 21	
	Emissivity of insulation	e_i	0.94	STO 22	
	Calculation factor	—	0.7	STO 24	
				A	
3.	Run program				
4.	Intermediate printed output is surface-temperature estimates				T_2
5.	Final printout is:				
	Final surface temperature, °F	T_2			115.2
	Heat loss, Btu/(h)(ft)	Q			97.63

The output tape for the above example is:

```
102.4386873
111.7797835
115.0801303
115.1713215

115.1713315
97.63171797
```

References

1. Brown, G. G., et al., "Unit Operations," John Wiley & Sons, Inc., New York, 1950, pp. 427, 444, 459, 460 & 584.
2. CertainTeed Corp. Bulletin, "850° Snap-on Fiberglass Pipe Insulation," Mar. 1978.
3. Armstrong Cork Co., "Accotherm Pipe Insulation," Bulletin 15P, Nov. 1977.

The author

Frank S. Schroder is an Engineering Specialist in the Central Research Engineering Department, 3M Center, PO Box 33221, St. Paul, MN 55133; tel: 612-733-1657. He received a B.S. degree in chemical engineering from Michigan Technological University, Houghton, Mich. and previously worked for Union Carbide, Silicones Div.

Insulation without economics

To calculate the economic thickness of insulation,
you must predict such items as future interest
rates and fuel costs. It may be more
reasonable to calculate an
"acceptable heat-loss"
thickness.

M. McChesney and P. McChesney, Fuel Save Associates

☐ Thermal insulation
should be the simplest, most
generally accepted, cost-effective
method of saving energy immediately available to a
plant owner. However this clearly is not the case to
many—perhaps too many—owners, because to them it
is just another capital investment; as such its purchase
must ensure a return on the investment.

Their argument is simple and direct: if the plant
owner can make a 17% profit on his salable products
whereas insulation returns only, say, 12%, then surely it
makes no economic sense to buy the insulation—since
the more profitable thing to do is to expand plant capacity to produce more salable products.

Having reached this conclusion, the plant owner then
can salve his conscience by reducing energy wastage
solely by "good housekeeping" involving minimal or
even no capital expenditure. After all, there is no short-
age of advice and guidance available on how to save
10% of plant energy bills without spending *any* money!

Economic thickness of insulation (ETI)

Because of this "economic" attitude toward insulation, it became necessary to evaluate how much was

actually "economic,"
and this gave rise to the concept
of the "economic thickness of insula-
tion." This concept has been extensively discussed on
both sides of the Atlantic, being analyzed in the technical literature over the years. There are now lengthy
books and manuals available that show the (sometimes
bemused) plant owner how to calculate this economic
thickness by using tables, graphs or computers. All the
plant engineer needs to do. is to input data into the
tables, etc., and out comes the "economic thickness."

In the U.S.A., the history of the tables highlights their
problems. In 1949 a committee was established by
Union Carbide Corp. and West Virginia University to
reduce the economic-thickness calculation to a simple
procedure in which, following the McMillan analysis
[4], the heat factors were separated from the cost factors. A manual was produced by a forerunner of TIMA
(Thermal Insulation Manufacturers Assn.), with nomographs and charts; TIMA itself apparently produced its
own version around 1960.

Since that time the data and their presentation un-
derwent modification and, around 1973, programs
called ECON-I (tables, charts, worked examples),

ECON-II (marketing manual) and R-ECON (retrofitting) became available. However it was felt by some that these programs had averaged too many variables to nominal values and, in addition, the minimum insulation depreciation (amortization) period was too long. This last objection is important since it showed that plant owners were *not* prepared to regard insulation as a long-term investment—an attitude that is still common today.

Insulation, if properly maintained, can have a very long lifetime (30 years or more) but the pipework around which it is placed may be part of a plant that rapidly becomes obsolescent. Since in many cases insulation is not recovered, but scrapped, it makes no sense to amortize it over a longer period of time.

Accordingly, around 1976 a refinement of these tables was produced by York Research Corp. for the Federal Energy Administration and called ETI (Economic Thickness for Industrial Insulation). It consisted of 10 sections covering fuel costs (which had become a major consideration since the 1974 OPEC price rise), insulation costs, condensation control and retrofitting. All the information was given in tabular, graphical or nomographical form and also in a mathematical appendix.

However, this apparently was not suitable for all needs, and from 1976 to 1980 numerous suggestions were made to make the ETI program more useful. A recent revision has been made incorporating these suggestions, as a joint venture between TIMA, NICA (National Insulation Contractors Assn.) and Louisiana Technical University, the resulting manuals being called ETIH (Economical Thickness of Insulation for Hot Surfaces) and ETIC (Cold Surfaces).

Difficulties with calculating ETI

Over the years, the senior writer has used these tables and watched the brave attempts to present the calculational procedure in a digestible form without sacrificing too much accuracy. Undeniably the use of discounted-cash-flow analysis does complicate the calculation, and the incorporation of future fuel-price increases adds further difficulty. Possibly because of the complexity of these economic factors (but this is only a guess), in the U.K. the Department of Energy produced a slim book of graphs showing the heat loss from unit lengths of pipes of various diameters carrying various thicknesses of different types of insulation and giving a calculational procedure for obtaining the economic thickness of insulation.

However, the book makes no allowance whatever for either discounted cash flows or future fuel-price increases. These graphs have the merit of simplicity, but the writers have found them inaccurate because they are plotted on log-log scales.

In this article we use several of the commonly adopted methods for calculating the economic thickness, and show that a real dilemma arises in trying to decide what is the actual thickness that is *economic*. In fact, we wonder whether there is such a quantity at all!

Put another way, we have a sneaking suspicion that the "economic" thickness of insulation is more or less what any plant engineer wants it to be. The reason is twofold: there are inevitably uncertainties attached to the heat-input data, but these can be controlled to a considerably greater extent than the uncertainties (or, put more euphemistically, the greater range of choice) in the economic-data inputs. Thereafter we propose a simple criterion for determining the *sensible* thickness of insulation (not economic thickness, since economics is taken right out of the problem altogether, at least in explicit form), that puts the decision-making back where it really belongs—in the hands of the plant engineer and not of the company accountant!

A full analysis of insulation economics requires that at least 20 input-data variables be assigned; these can be grouped under four headings for the case of pipe insulation.

Insulation factors

1. Cost of installed insulation, of thickness t, per linear foot $C_{I(t)}$.
2. Thermal conductivity of insulation, k_I.
3. Thermal resistance of insulation surface, R_S.
4. Pipe diameter (nominal), d_1.
5. Ambient temperature, θ_3.
6. Ambient wind speed.
7. Pipe temperature, θ_1.
8. Amortization period of insulation, n.
9. Pipe-complexity factor.
10. Maintenance and insurance costs.

For simplicity we shall assume a pipe-complexity factor of unity, ignore maintenance and insurance costs, and assume zero wind speed.

Fuel factors

11. Type of fuel and cost, C_F.
12. Expected annual price rise of fuel expressed as a decimal, f.

Heat-producing-plant factors

13. Efficiency of conversion of fuel to heat, E.
14. Number of hours of operation per year, N.
15. Capital investment in heat-producing plant.
16. Amortization period of heat-producing plant.

For simplicity we shall completely ignore the economic aspects of the heat-producing plant. Normally the existence of insulation can reduce the size of the needed heat-producing plant, and this represents an incremental positive cash flow. We make the simplifying assumption that the decision to insulate does not affect the plant capacity—as would be the case for insulation retrofit.

Economic factors

17. Cost of money, i.e., return on investment in insulation required, i.
18. Tax rate.
19. Cost of money to finance heat-producing plant.

Nomenclature

A_I	External surface area of insulation jacketing, ft²
A_P	External surface area of bare pipe, ft²
C_F	Cost of fuel, 2.83×10^{-6}, $ per Btu
$C_{H(t)}$	Total cost of heat loss per linear foot of pipe covered with insulation of thickness t, for an entire operational year, $ ft⁻¹ yr⁻¹ for money valued at this moment of time $$= \frac{NC_F}{E}\frac{Q_{(t)}}{L}$$
$C_{I(t)}$	Cost of installed insulation per linear foot of pipe, of thickness t_I inches, $ ft⁻¹ for money valued at this moment of time
d_1	Nominal diameter of pipe, ft
d_2	Nominal outer diameter of insulation jacketing, ft
E	Efficiency of conversion of fuel to heat expressed as a decimal, 0.83
f	Annual increase in the cost of fuel expressed as a decimal, 0.1
F	Heat-loss rate per ft² of insulated pipe divided by heat-loss rate per ft² of same pipe bare of insulation
h_C	Convective heat-transfer coefficient of insulation surface jacketing for still air, Btu h⁻¹ ft⁻² °F⁻¹
h_I	Total surface heat-transfer coefficient of insulation surface jacketing for still air, Btu h⁻¹ ft⁻² °F⁻¹
h_P	Total surface heat-transfer coefficient of bare pipe for still air, Btu h⁻¹ ft⁻² °F⁻¹
h_R	Radiative heat-transfer coefficient of insulation surface jacketing for still air, Btu h⁻¹ ft⁻² °F⁻¹

i	Cost of money; return on investment required expressed as a decimal
k_I	Thermal conductivity of the pipe insulation, Btu ft h⁻¹ ft⁻² °F⁻¹
L	Length of pipe, ft
n	Amortization period of the insulation (number of years over which the insulation economics is to be evaluated), years
N	Number of hours of operation of the fuel-to-heat conversion equipment per year, 8,760 h
$Q_{(t)}$	Rate of heat loss from pipe covered with insulation of thickness t_I inches, Btu h⁻¹
r_1	Nominal radius of the pipe, ft
r_2	Nominal radius of insulation plus jacketing, ft
R_I	Thermal resistance of the insulation and its jacketing, h ft² °F (Btu)⁻¹
R_P	Thermal resistance of the bare pipe surface, h ft² °F (Btu)⁻¹
R_S	Thermal resistance of the insulation jacket surface, h ft² °F (Btu)⁻¹
t	Thickness of insulation and jacketing, in.
[USPWF]	Uniform-series-present-worth factor, $$\frac{(1+i)^n - 1}{i(1+i)^n}$$
ε	Surface emissivity of the insulation surface jacketing or of the bare pipe, 0.9
θ_1	Temperature of steam in pipe: also temperature of pipe wall, °F
θ_2	Temperature of insulation surface jacketing, °F
θ_3	Temperature of still air (70°F)
σ	Stefan's radiation constant, 0.171×10^{-8} Btu h⁻¹ ft⁻² °R⁻⁴

20. Economic model used for determining the economic thickness of insulation.

It must be stressed that the simplifications that we make in no way detract from the overall conclusions drawn. What they do is avoid obscuring the important issues in a morass of arithmetic—they alter number values but not decisions.

The heat-loss equations

Referring to Fig. 1, consider a horizontal pipe of nominal diameter d_1, covered with insulation of thickness t, and of thermal conductivity k_I, carrying dry saturated steam at temperature θ_1. Even with insulation present, the pipe will lose heat, and in the steady state, when the surface temperature of the insulation does not change, the rate at which heat is lost per linear foot of the pipe is:

$$\frac{Q_{(t)}}{L} = \frac{\theta_1 - \theta_3}{\frac{1}{2\pi k_I}\ln(d_2/d_1) + \frac{1}{\pi d_2 h_I}} \quad (1)$$

Strictly, this equation is a simplification because:
■ It assumes that the convective heat-transfer coeffi-

cient from steam to the inner wall of the pipe is infinitely large compared with h_I, the sum of the convective and radiative heat-transfer coefficients from the insulation surface to the ambient air. This is an excellent approximation because any heat loss from the steam will cause it to condense, and the condensation heat-transfer coefficient (for film-wise condensation) lies in the range 1,000–2,000 Btu hr⁻¹ ft⁻² °F⁻¹, which is about one thousand times greater than h_I.

■ It ignores the thermal resistance of the pipe wall, which is usually an excellent approximation in most heat-transfer cases other than thick-walled vats.

In Eq. (1) the value of h_I is given by:

$$h_I = h_C + h_R$$

where:

$$h_C = 0.270(\theta_2 - \theta_3)^{0.25} d_2^{-0.25} \quad (2)$$
$$h_R = \varepsilon\sigma[(\theta_2 + 460) + (\theta_3 + 460)] \times [(\theta_2 + 460)^2 + (\theta_3 + 460)^2] \quad (3)$$

Clearly, to evaluate Eq. (2) and (3) we need to know the value of the insulation surface temperature θ_2. The calculation and importance of θ_2 have been described

Winterizing process plants

Maintaining fluid temperatures without overheating is a problem in many CPI plants. Here are techniques to provide effective protection while keeping costs down. Included is an update on materials, and an explanation of some of the pitfalls that await the unwary.

E. Fisch, The Halcon SD Group, Inc.

☐ The need to winterize chemical-process-industries (CPI) plants to prevent freezing or undesirable condensation has long been recognized.

Over the years, the procedures for winterizing, as well as the required installation techniques, have been reduced almost to "cookbook" standards. Recently, however, certain changes have mandated a more thorough analysis of winterizing procedures. These include:

1. The rising cost of all forms of energy and, in particular, a great emphasis on conservation of steam, so as to avoid costly boiler additions.

2. Increasing field-labor costs, and the increasing availability of pretraced or preinsulated tubing components and custom-designed, preformed insulation and housings, particularly for various types of instruments.

3. Development of easy-to-use, reliable electrical tracing systems and components, as well as a change in the relative costs of electricity and steam in many areas.

4. Increased automation of plants, which makes less manpower available for inspection and adjustment of tracing systems.

5. A greater use of electronic instrumentation, which is more susceptible to damage from overheating arising from the use of tracing systems.

Winterization techniques

There are five basic winterizing techniques:

1. Designing and operating systems so as to avoid the need for protection against freezing. This includes design techniques—e.g., the inclusion of self-draining lines and warmup bypasses, valve placement, and operating procedures intended to drain stagnant lines or ensure continuity of flow.

2. Heat tracing using steam, electricity or circulating liquids as the heat source.

3. Installating internal heating coils.

4. Locating systems within heated buildings or non-freezing environments.

5. Adding only insulation, to provide protection for lines with low flowrates.

System design and operation

Owing to the high costs of installing and operating heat tracing, it is worth making the additional effort to eliminate unnecessary tracing, and worth incurring the costs of modifications that make tracing unnecessary. Among the techniques:

Bypass lines — Bypass lines may be added around equipment to maintain circulation when block valves are closed for equipment maintenance. This is an almost universally applicable method for winterizing cooling-water systems, considering these factors:

■ Cooling-water-circulation systems are, for all practical purposes, as reliable as steam systems. They normally employ multiple pumps and often include spare pumps with steam turbine drives, or alternative power feeders to ensure reliability.

■ Cooling water can be circulated during maintenance operations, without flammability or toxicity hazards.

■ There is generally sufficient freeboard in cooling-tower sumps to drain headers in an extreme emergency.

■ Under certain circumstances, e.g., when using water for cooling pump seals and bearings, the addition of bypass lines may interfere with maintenance, and the use of tracing on these small lines may also raise the temperatures to undesirable levels. In these cases, block valves should be located at the headers or the subheaders to protect the water supply lines when the pumps must be removed for service. At such times, small amounts of water must be drained from the lines.

Recirculation lines — Recirculation lines may be provided to maintain backflow through the non-operating pumps. This is illustrated in Fig. 1. This technique, in principle, applies to all pumps handling fluids substantially above their freezing points. However, the practice should be limited to more critical systems such as condensate pumps, cooling water pumps and continuously running flush or seal pumps. In these services, pump stoppage generally becomes immediately apparent to the operators, and starting of the spare pump would have a high priority. Further, these systems are generally kept in operation, even during shutdowns.

A similar result may be achieved by drilling a hole in the pump-discharge check valves. This practice requires special care during installation and maintenance to ensure that the check valve (or its replacement) does indeed have the required hole.

Elimination of some tracing — Tracing may be eliminated on lines that are self-draining and that contain fluids not very close to their freezing points.

Diaphragm seals — Diaphragm seals may be used for instruments on lines that would not otherwise require steam tracing.

Dip pipes — Internal dip pipes, rather than external loop seals, may be used in vessels.

Block valve location — Block valves may be placed so as to eliminate dead legs or permit lines to be self-draining. This requires coordination with operational procedures to drain lines at shutdowns or when they are not in use. This is an operational judgment, balancing operating-labor availability versus cost savings. Lines that often fall into this category include:

■ Startup and rerun lines that would require the inclusion of double blocks and bleeds, if these are not already needed for other reasons.

■ Long product-transfer lines that normally stay in operation as long as the plant is running.

Use of traps — Traps may be used in steam lines to prevent accumulation of condensate even when block valves are closed (since eventually they will leak).

Common insulation of warm and cold lines — This, of course, can only be done if there is assurance that the warm line will always remain warm, as in the case of steam and condensate lines at hose stations. A typical arrangement is shown in Fig. 2.

Use of thermosyphon circulation — Tracing may be eliminated where advantage can be taken of thermosyphon circulation. This technique can be used for pump seal piping and for some level instruments.

Heat tracing

Unless another reliable method of winterization is used, heat tracing is required to provide the necessary protection against heat loss. Generally, heat tracing provides protection against winter temperatures, but it may be required all year round, or even indoors, if the temperatures to be maintained are high enough.

Although this article is largely devoted to heat tracing techniques, it should be recognized that the installation and operating costs of heat tracing are considerable, and

alternative techniques should be used wherever feasible to minimize these costs. J. T. Lonsdale and J. E. Mundy [1], have shown costs on the order of $15/ft for installation of the steam distribution and condensate collection systems, and $20/ft for the actual tracing, *plus* $4.23/(yr)(ft) for maintenance and operating costs (assuming steam at $5/1,000 lb, and an operating time of 8,760 h/yr). The saving resulting from eliminating even 100 ft of steam tracing comes to:

Installation cost	$2,000
Capital equivalent of 3-yr operating costs	1,300
Total equivalent capital	$3,300

If elimination of the tracing avoids the need for insulation, or if the tracing requires the use of heat transfer cement, the saving in installation cost would be 30 to 50% greater than noted above.

Internal coils and tracers

The design of internal coils for winterizing of tanks and vessels is, in principle, similar to the design of heat tracing systems. However, detailed design procedures are outside the scope of this article. This topic has been thoroughly covered by D. K. Kumana and S. P. Kothari [2].

Internal tracers are used to a limited degree. These have been employed for many years on transfer lines carrying heavy crudes, or similar materials. However, the potential for leaks into the process stream, as well as the impossibility of inspecting joints in the tracer, make this technique relatively impractical. Furthermore, the development of heat transfer cement has provided better means of maintaining high process temperatures with external tracing.

Heated buildings

The location of plants or equipment within heated buildings, or the running of piping inside heated ductwork, is occasionally a valid means of winterizing equipment and piping. This is often done for limited areas such as centrifuge rooms, analyzer rooms, water wells, etc., so as to avoid the costs of tracing, as well as to provide weather protection for operation or maintenance. In extreme cases, such as under subarctic conditions, entire plants may be enclosed.

In either case, when flammable or noxious materials are present, consideration must be given both to providing adequate ventilation (and the heating of makeup air), and to considering the need for, and cost of, upgrading the electrical hazard classification from Div. II (flammable vapors present only in the event of mishap) to Div. I (flammable vapors normally present).

The burial of lines and valves is also used, and is almost universally applied for winterizing fire-water and drinking-water lines. However, the burial of process lines is generally not suitable because of potential hazards in the event of leakage.

Insulation

Adding insulation, without steam tracing, is an economical way to provide against freezing. Generally, local experience will indicate if the approach is feasible. Conventional heat-loss calculations described later in this article can also be used. An additional check can be made by using published tables of time for freezing in a stagnant line, such as those of F. F. House [3]. In evaluating the use of insulation for winterizing, the expected period of low flow or flow interruption should be considered. This is especially important for small-diameter lines, which will freeze more rapidly than larger ones.

Design—systems review

The importance of a thorough review of the systems to ensure adequate winterization cannot be overemphasized. Failure to provide adequate systems, or failure to operate them properly, will result in freezing or undesirable condensation. These can damage piping, instruments and equipment, and interrupt plant operation.

Attention to winterization must be given at all stages of a project—from inception to engineering flowsheets (or piping and instrument diagrams), and then to detailed engineering design and installation. Finally, the systems must be adequately tested in conjunction with the overall plant-commissioning procedures before being placed in operation.

Stage I: Establishing basic criteria

A review of both process and utility systems is necessary to establish winterizing requirements and applicable temperature criteria.

First, the tracing criteria for the various systems are selected, including type of tracing (steam or electric), need for heat transfer cement or spacers, required steam pressures or electric-heat input rates, as well as maximum temperature limitations for both the items being traced and the tracing materials.

Then, an initial evaluation is made of the application of techniques other than tracing; this is further refined and finalized during the preparation of the piping and instrumentation diagrams.

The evaluation of temperature limitations of both the process materials and the tracers themselves should be made at this preliminary stage to ensure that proper selections of tracing systems are made—from both technical and economic viewpoints. Among the guidelines to be established:

Heat stability — The stability of the process material to the tracing medium temperatures during periods of low flow should be considered. This will indicate the maximum heating-medium temperature, as well as any need for spacers. It may even dictate that a low-pressure steam tracer with heat transfer cement should be used, even though a higher-pressure steam tracer without heat transfer cement would be less costly and would provide the necessary protection against freezing. When corrosive materials are being handled, the exposure of the piping itself to higher temperatures (and attendant higher corrosion rates) can also be significant.

Maximum temperatures — The maximum process temperatures to which the tracer will be exposed will dictate the selection of the tracer material.

Process temperatures should take into account the possibility of hot water flushing, or steaming out, of lines, that could expose the tracers to temperatures

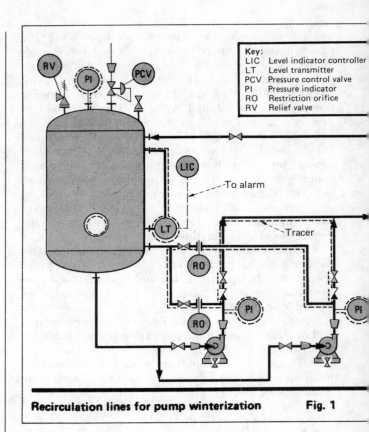

Key:
LIC   Level indicator controller
LT   Level transmitter
PCV   Pressure control valve
PI   Pressure indicator
RO   Restriction orifice
RV   Relief valve

Recirculation lines for pump winterization   Fig. 1

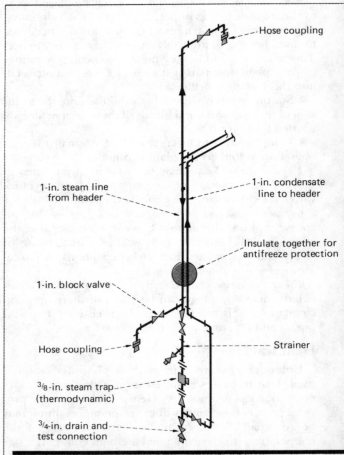

Typical use of common insulation for winterizing   Fig. 2

higher than the anticipated process operating (or other normally expected) temperatures.

The upper limit for using copper tubing is 400°F (equivalent to 250-psig steam). Above this temperature, steel tubing or pipe is required. Copper tubing is widely used when high-temperature materials are not required, because of the ease with which it is bent, and its resistance to scale formation in the system. However, the availability and cost of copper varies, so at various times steel tracers are used instead, particularly outside the U.S. This can be done either by the total substitution of steel tubing for copper tubing, or by using mostly steel or iron pipe (with copper tubing sections retained for valve wrapping and for other applications where appreciable bending is required).

When electric tracers are used, the process temperatures should be included in the requisitions issued to suppliers to ensure that the proper tracer type is selected. The widely used temperature-limiting type of tracer is generally available in several grades, with typical limitation ranges of 150–175°F, 200–250°F, and temperatures up to 500°F. Electric tracers of the resistance type, generally used for higher-temperature applications, also require that the designer consider maximum temperatures, so that the appropriate sheath and electrical insulation materials will be used.

Ambient conditions — In establishing the winterizing requirements, the selection of the minimum-temperature/maximum-wind-velocity combination also requires careful attention. The minimum winter temperature used for building heating design is *not* suitable as the basis for process winterization design. The selection of the building design temperatures often includes an economic balance of excessive equipment cost versus the relatively minor, infrequent and short-term inconvenience of an underheated building. The economic consequences of a single short-term freezeup of even a few process lines are serious enough to call for "once in a century" minimum temperatures as the basis of process-system winterization design.

In establishing the basic design criteria for the plant, adequate provision should be made for utilities requirements for heat tracing; these are often neglected. A quick guideline for estimating steam tracing requirements allows 10 lb/h of steam usage for each tracer, with one tracer required for every 60–70 ft of traced pipe. (This allows for tracing of instruments as well as piping, and includes distribution losses and normal trap leakage.) Power requirements for electric tracing of piping carrying water-like materials are typically 3 to 6 watts/ft of traced pipe for the normal operating load, with a peak load of 5 to 10 watts/ft.

With higher-freezing-point materials, the electric-power and steam consumption requirements could be considerably greater, since a large number of lines could require multiple tracers.

Stage II: Reviewing P&I diagrams

The flowsheets should show the type and extent of tracing, including instruments, lines that require makeup of heat losses during normal operation, and lines that require freeze protection during maintenance shutdowns. Such would include process lines, service or process-water lines, safety-shower supply lines, steam and condensate lines not otherwise protected, non-self-draining steam traps or liquid drainers, high-pourpoint fuel oil lines, etc.

The flowsheets should be carefully reviewed to identify and show tracing on the normally stagnant portions of lines where design alternatives or operational procedures cannot eliminate tracing. Note particularly:

■ Pumps that are spared, up to and including block valves.

■ Spare filters, or similar devices that are spared.

■ Control valve or meter bypasses, and nondrainable portions of control valve or meter stations.

■ Instrument leads, and instruments on liquid and gas lines that contain liquid that may freeze or condensable vapors. This includes instruments both on lines and on equipment in steam, steam condensate, cooling water, compressed air or hot vapor service.

■ Instruments on vessels or towers, including level transmitters and gage glasses, pressure and differential transmitters and gages (together with their leads).

■ Sample taps and sampling systems.

Note that for sampling systems and differential-pressure transmitters in gas or vapor service, the criterion for heat tracing is normally to prevent condensation, rather than to avoid freezing.

■ Pressure and vacuum relief valves and gage hatches.

■ Seal pots.

■ Nondraining portions of lines, such as loop seals (unless special operating provisions are made for draining at shutdown). Note that plans must be made for continuously refilling critical loop seals or seal pots, since tracing may vaporize the liquid in the seal.

The flowsheets should include all provisions for alternatives to tracing, where needed. Items that should be shown on flowsheets include:

■ Lines that should be selfdraining.

■ Minimum-flow bypasses.

■ Recirculation lines (or drilled check valves) at pumps.

■ Traps in steam lines not provided with header block-valves and drains.

■ Header block valves and adequate drains in steam lines, and in condensate lines that are not traced.

■ Limits of enclosures and underground line risers.

■ Double block and bleed valves.

■ Block valve locations, where necessary for winterization. These must be supplemented by appropriate drains—it must be assumed that block valves will leak.

■ Instrument location notes, where close coupling or free drainage is necessary for winterizing.

■ Seal diaphragms on instruments.

■ Lines to be insulated together.

■ Items to be connected to emergency power, such as critical electric tracers or enclosure heaters.

At this time, the preliminary evaluations of alternative winterizing techniques (made during the initial process design) should be finalized.

Stage III: Detailed design and review

Items that should particularly be checked during the reviews of the piping design drawings or model include:

■ Location of maintenance block valves and minimum-

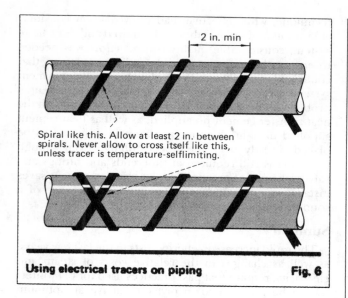

Spiral like this. Allow at least 2 in. between spirals. Never allow to cross itself like this, unless tracer is temperature-selflimiting.

2 in. min

Using electrical tracers on piping   Fig. 6

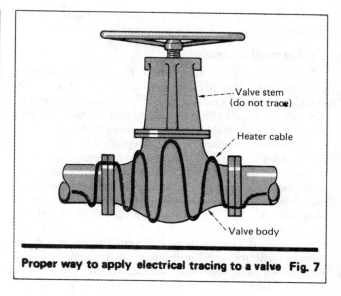

Valve stem (do not trace)

Heater cable

Valve body

Proper way to apply electrical tracing to a valve Fig. 7

nature, each section must be specifically designed to be a fixed length with a predetermined resistance, selected to yield a desired heat rate that is constant over its entire length. The tracing system requires fairly accurate pre-engineering, and factory assembly of custom designed sections. Field modification is generally impractical, and maintaining inventories of individual spare cables is often necessary. This type of tracer is subject to total failure in the event of conductor breakage (at even a single point) and is subject to burnout, particularly if overlapping is not avoided during installation. Thermostatic control is necessary to avoid process overheating and to reduce the frequency of burnout.

Despite their inherent disadvantages, series-resistance electric tracers are a suitable choice for high-temperature, high-input-rate tracing since their construction allows for the use of high-temperature insulating material, and conductors suitably sized to handle high currents.

Parallel-resistance cable

This style consists of two insulated parallel conductors wrapped with a fine-resistance-wire coil that is alternately fastened to each of the conductors at intervals of about 2 to 3 ft, depending on the desired heat-input rate. The conductors and resistance wire are then encased in a protective sheath.

Various sheath and insulating materials are available, as are variations in resistance wire size and contact intervals. These enable the making of heater tapes with maximum exposure temperatures ranging between 200 and 600°F, and heat input rates generally between 2 and 15 watts/ft. This type of tape is relatively flexible and can be used for wrapping valves and instruments but, like series-resistance cables, is subject to burnout at overlapping points.

Because of the parallel conductor construction, failure of one of the thin heating wires will cause loss of heat input over only a limited length. The parallel construction permits field cutting to the necessary length, and only limited preengineering is necessary. Since only parallel conductors have to carry the full current, the maximum length of tracer can often be 200 ft or more,

and the desired heat input is not appreciably affected by tracer length.

Since the heat input rate is constant, thermostatic control of surface temperatures is essential if overheating of the traced pipe is to be avoided.

Temperature-selflimiting heating tape

The most recently developed style of electric tracer cable is the selflimiting type. This style consists of two parallel conductors embedded in a semiconductive core, which has the unique property of rapidly increasing electrical resistance with increasing temperatures until the core material becomes nonconductive, stopping the generation of heat entirely. This "cutoff" temperature can be adjusted by changes in the formulation of the core material, and tapes are designed with maximum cutoff temperatures between 150 and 275°F.

This selflimiting feature has significant advantages. Local overheating can be avoided, and there is automatic conservation of power consumption as external temperatures and pipe flowrates vary, even if no thermostats are installed. This style of tape is specified with a nominal heat input rate at about 50°F. This nominal rate can be between about 3 and 30 watts/ft. Selflimiting heating tapes have maximum exposure limits, generally between 180 and 350°F, depending on the jacket material used. With appropriate selection of materials, this type of tape is also available with short-term limits as high as 500°F. These high-exposure temperature ratings are necessary when either steaming-out of lines, or other high-temperature short-term exposure, is anticipated.

The selflimiting construction of this style of tracer makes it essentially immune from burnout even if the tape is overlapped. Further, in the case of lower temperature ratings, this tape is quite thin and does not require any increase in diameter of the insulation, as would be necessary with steam tracers.

As with parallel-resistance heaters, tracer length has little effect on heat input rate. Maximum length can be 100 ft or more. However, since the electrical conductivity of the tape increases as the temperature drops, the power supply must allow for the current inrush during cold startups, and should have a capacity greater than the nominal rating of the tracing system.

Preformed accessories

For 15 years, there has been an increasing availability of preformed and preinsulated accessories for use in steam, electric or circulating-fluid heat tracing systems. Because these accessories reduce labor and time, and result in more reliable and more easily maintained systems, they have gained wide acceptance for both new plant construction and maintenance in existing plants. These accessories fall into the following main categories:

Instrument enclosures — In addition to conventional insulated meter boxes, premolded foam insulation is available that has been specifically designed to fit various types of instruments, particularly pressure gages and many styles of transmitters. Different shapes to suit the various vendors' specific models can be supplied, and have preformed holes for valves, drains, etc. They can be obtained with either an electrically-heated or a steam-heated element designed to provide protection against freezing without exposing the instruments to excessive temperatures.

Besides providing freeze protection, these enclosures protect against corrosion and splashes. Most important, they can easily be removed without damage, and are available for quick reinstallation at the conclusion of recalibration or other maintenance operations.

Pretraced tubing and tubing bundles — Pretraced, preinsulated and prejacketed tubing and tubing bundles are frequently the most cost-effective choice for tracing instrument impulse lines, analyzer taps, sample connections or other small-diameter lines, and for use as steam supply and condensate return leads.

Bundles are available with a single tube, or with multiple tubes of various sizes and materials. The multiple tubes are available with the tubes in contact, or separated with a layer of insulation to prevent overheating. In addition, preinsulated bundles with electrical tracing are also available, having the tracers of the temperature self-limiting type or constant-heat-input type, with or without thermostatic control.

The most commonly used bundle combinations are:
- ⅜-in. copper tube (for steam) with either one ½-in. 316 SS tube (for pressure meters or sample lines) or two ½-in. 316 SS tubes (for flow meters).
- ½-in. copper tube for steam supply and condensate runs between manifolds and users.

Bundles with two, three or four ⅜-in. copper tubes are also occasionally used for steam supply and condensate collection lines. Bundles with two ⅜-in. copper tubes and one ½-in. 316 SS tube are also useful for tracing instrument impulse lines, so that the same bundle can be used for steam tracing and condensate return.

Use of the preinsulated bundles greatly reduces the amount of labor and inconvenience in handling loose insulation materials, and the bundles are particularly advantageous in maintenance work, since the tracers are almost immediately available for use.

Preapplied heat transfer cement

When heat transfer cements were first introduced, they were formulated to be applied by troweling. This technique, while effective, had drawbacks. A considerable amount of skilled labor was required and, for a large system, considerable quality-control effort was needed to ensure the absence of voids and other defects that could lead to cold spots. Preapplied heat transfer cement systems were developed to overcome these potential problems. These include heating panels or coils with the heat transfer cement preapplied, as well as heat cement supplied in light sheet-metal channels designed to be placed directly over the tracer tubing. Even though troweling is still required at tube ends and fittings and valves, the use of preapplied heat transfer cement saves installation costs and provides greater assurance of a sound installation.

Summary

The rapid increase in energy costs in the last few years, as well as changes in the relative costs of steam and electricity, require that past practices used for CPI winterization be reevaluated in order to arrive at optimum designs. Because of higher energy costs, greater use should be made of winterization techniques not based on heat tracing. Where tracing is required, sound design requires careful evaluation of the relative merits of steam, electricity and other heating media, as well as the savings that can be made by using recent developments in heat tracing materials. These can lead to substantial cost savings, not only in new plant construction but in the maintenance of existing plants. Also, newly developed materials and accessories offer additional savings as well as increased effectiveness and reliability.

Acknowledgment

The author wishes to acknowledge the assistance of his colleagues at Scientific Design Co., not only in the preparation of this article but for their efforts over the years in evaluating new techniques and developing improved specifications and more effective procedures for plant winterization.

References

1. Lonsdale, J. T., and Mundy, J. E., Estimating Pipe Heat Tracing Costs, *Chem. Eng.*, Nov. 29, 1982, p. 89.
2. Kumana, D. K., and Kothari S. P., Predict Storage Tank Heat Transfer Precisely, *Chem. Eng.*, Mar. 22, 1982, p. 127.
3. House, F. F., Winterizing Chemical Plants, *Chem. Eng.*, Sept. 11, 1967, p. 177.
4. Ibid, p. 173.
5. Blackwell, W. W., Estimate Heat Tracing Requirements for Pipelines, *Chem. Eng.*, Sept. 6, 1982, p. 115.

The author

Eugene Fisch is a project manager at The Halcon SD Group's Scientific Design division, 2 Park Ave., New York, NY 10016, tel. (212) 689-3000, where he has been engaged for more thant 30 years in a variety of activities associated with the design and construction of chemical plants worldwide. He holds a B.S. degree in chemical engineering from City College of New York, and is a licensed professional engineer in New York.

Estimate heat-tracing requirements for pipelines

Because the equations for tracing contain two unknown quantities, this calculator program contains a rapid procedure for determining the film heat-transfer coefficient to air. The program then continues to establish the remaining design values for heat tracing.

W. Wayne Blackwell, Ford, Bacon & Davis, Texas Inc.

☐ Pipelines containing liquids are often heat-traced to prevent the liquids from freezing or becoming too viscous to flow. Pipelines handling gases are sometimes heat-traced to prevent components or water vapor in the gases from condensing.

The program to be described will allow us to rapidly calculate the heat loss and tracing requirements for any given pipeline, using hot oil or other fluid medium as the heat source for the tracer. The program was written for the Texas Instruments TI-59 programmable calculator, to be used with the PC-100C printer.

This line-tracing program:
- Calculates surface temperature of insulated pipe.
- Calculates heat transferred per 100 ft of pipe.
- Calculates total heat transferred.
- Determines flowrate for hot media.
- Estimates number of heat tracers required without heat-transfer cement.
- Estimates number of heat tracers required with heat-transfer cement.

The program can be used without the printer because most results are stored in the TI-59 registers.

Equations for heat, flow and temperature

The program solves the following equations[†]:

$$Q = 2\pi K_i (T_a - T_s)/\ln(d_o/d_i) \tag{1}$$

$$Q = h_a(\pi d_o/12)(T_s - T_{air}) \tag{2}$$

$$X = \ln(d_o/d_i)(h_a)(d_o/12)/2K_i \tag{3}$$

$$T_s = (T_a + XT_{air})/(X + 1) \tag{4}$$

$$Q_t = QL_L \tag{5}$$

$$W = Q_t/C_p(T_{mi} - T_{mo}) \tag{6}$$

$$T_{woc} = Q/a(T_{med.avg.} - T_p) \tag{7}$$

$$T_{wc} = Q/b(T_{med.avg.} - T_p) \tag{8}$$

[†]Eq. (1) and (2) are from Ref. 1; Eq. (7) and (8), Ref. 2; and Eq. (9), Ref. 3.

$$h_c + h_r = 564/(d_o)^{0.19}[273 - (T_s - T_{air})] \tag{9}$$

$$W_F = A + B(T_s - T_{air}) + C(T_s - T_{air})^2 \tag{10}$$

$$h_a = (h_c + h_r)W_F \tag{11}$$

Kern [1] and others have demonstrated that the heat transferred through an insulated pipe encounters four resistances: (1) film resistance on inside wall of pipe, (2) heat resistance through pipe wall, (3) heat resistance through insulation, and (4) air film resistance on outside of insulation. The first two resistances are normally very small, and have been neglected in this program.

For this program, Eq. (1) and (2) were equated, and the terms rearranged to form Eq. (4). Since Eq. (3) and (4) involve two unknowns (h_a and T_s), an initial value of h_a is assumed and T_s calculated. The program then calculates a new value of h_a from Eq. (9), and Eq. (4) is resolved for a new T_s. This procedure is repeated until the film heat-transfer coefficient changes less than 0.01 from the previous calculation.

After T_s has been determined, the program continues to calculate Q, W, and the number of tracers, with and without transfer cement, required to maintain pipeline temperatures. Heat losses are based on a 20-mph wind speed, but may be adjusted for zero wind speed, as will shortly be explained.

Using the program

Table I lists the detailed program-operating instructions. After entry of the program (Steps 000 to 361) into program memory, and entry of the required constants in Storage Registers 18, 19, 20, 23, 24 and 25 (as outlined in Table III), the program and contents of the storage registers are down-loaded onto magnetic cards. Once this information has been thus stored, the program is ready for use.

The user need only read in the magnetic cards, store pertinent data in Storage Registers 0 through 10, and press **A** to begin the calculations (Table II). Usually a first guess of about 4 for h_a speeds up convergence and

Originally published September 6, 1982

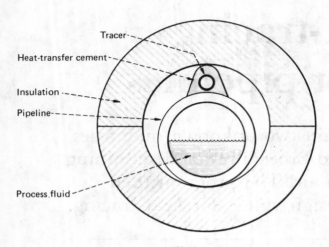

Single tracer

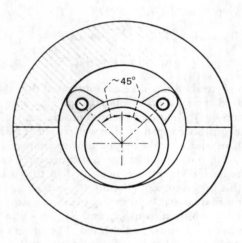

Two tracers

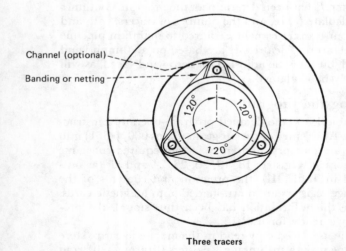

Three tracers

Configuration for heat tracers depends on number required

Program for calculating total heat transferred, flowrate

Step	Code	Key	Step	Code	Key	Step	Code	Key
	Start program		059	11	11	120	54	)
			060	55	÷	121	95	=
000	76	LBL	061	43	RCL	122	35	1/X
001	11	P	062	12	12	123	65	×
002	69	OP	063	95	=	124	05	5
003	00	00	064	23	LNX	125	06	6
004	43	RCL	065	65	×	126	04	4
005	18	18	066	43	RCL	127	95	=
006	69	OP	067	10	10	128	42	STO
007	01	01	068	65	×	129	22	22
008	43	RCL	069	43	RCL	130	43	RCL
009	19	19	070	11	11	131	14	14
010	69	OP	071	55	÷	132	75	-
011	02	02	072	01	1	133	43	RCL
012	43	RCL	073	02	2	134	04	04
013	20	20	074	55	÷	135	95	=
014	69	OP	075	02	2	136	42	STO
015	03	03	076	55	÷	137	27	27
016	69	OP	077	43	RCL	138	43	RCL
017	05	05	078	08	08			
018	43	RCL	079	95	=		Calculate wind factor	
019	02	02	080	42	STO			
020	85	+	081	16	16	139	23	23
021	43	RCL	082	65	×	140	42	STO
022	03	03	083	43	RCL	141	26	26
023	95	=	084	04	04	142	43	RCL
024	55	÷	085	85	+	143	27	27
025	02	2	086	43	RCL	144	65	×
026	95	=	087	13	13	145	43	RCL
027	42	STO	088	95	=	146	24	24
028	21	21	089	55	÷	147	95	=
029	85	+	090	53	(	148	44	SUM
030	43	RCL	091	43	RCL	149	26	26
031	01	01	092	16	16	150	43	RCL
032	95	=	093	85	+	151	27	27
033	55	÷	094	01	1	152	33	X²
034	02	2	095	54	)	153	65	×
035	95	=	096	95	=	154	43	RCL
036	42	STO	097	42	STO	155	25	25
037	13	13	098	14	14	156	95	=
038	43	RCL	099	76	LBL	157	44	SUM
039	05	05	100	13	C	158	26	26
040	85	+				159	43	RCL
041	43	RCL		Calculate $h_c + h_r$		160	26	26
042	06	06				161	65	×
043	95	=	101	43	RCL	162	43	RCL
044	42	STO	102	11	11	163	22	22
045	12	12	103	45	YX	164	95	=
046	85	+	104	93	.			
047	53	(	105	01	1		Calculate h_a	
048	43	RCL	106	09	9			
049	07	07	107	95	=	165	42	STO
050	65	×	108	65	×	166	28	28
051	02	2	109	53	(	167	93	.
052	54	)	110	02	2	168	00	0
053	95	=	111	07	7	169	01	1
054	42	STO	112	03	3	170	32	X:T
055	11	11	113	75	-	171	43	RCL
056	76	LBL	114	53	(	172	10	10
057	12	B	115	43	RCL	173	75	-
			116	14	14	174	43	RCL
	Calculate T_s		117	75	-	175	28	28
			118	43	RCL	176	95	=
058	**43**	**RCL**	119	04	04	177	50	I×I

of heat-transfer medium, and number of heat tracers — Table I

Step	Code	Key
178	77	GE
179	15	E
180	76	LBL
181	14	D

Calculate variables

Step	Code	Key
182	69	OP
183	00	00
184	03	3
185	07	7
186	03	3
187	06	6
188	69	OP
189	04	04
190	43	RCL
191	14	14
192	69	OP
193	06	06
194	43	RCL
195	28	28
196	65	×
197	89	π
198	65	×
199	43	RCL
200	11	11
201	55	÷
202	01	1
203	02	2
204	65	×
205	53	(
206	43	RCL
207	14	14
208	75	-
209	43	RCL
210	04	04
211	54	)
212	95	=
213	42	STO
214	15	15
215	69	OP
216	00	00
217	03	3
218	04	4
219	69	OP
220	04	04
221	43	RCL
222	15	15
223	69	OP
224	06	06
225	01	1
226	04	4
227	03	3
228	07	7
229	04	4
230	01	1
231	02	2
232	03	3
233	69	OP
234	04	04
235	43	RCL
236	15	15
237	65	×
238	43	RCL
239	00	00
240	95	=
241	69	OP
242	06	06
243	55	÷
244	43	RCL
245	09	09
246	55	÷
247	53	(
248	43	RCL
249	02	02
250	75	-
251	43	RCL
252	03	03
253	54	)
254	95	=
255	42	STO
256	17	17
257	02	2
258	07	7
259	01	1
260	04	4
261	06	6
262	03	3
263	02	2
264	03	3
265	69	OP
266	04	04
267	43	RCL
268	17	17
269	69	OP
270	06	06
271	43	RCL
272	21	21
273	75	-
274	43	RCL
275	01	01
276	95	=
277	42	STO
278	29	29
279	65	×

Constant a

Step	Code	Key
280	93	.
281	03	3
282	09	9
283	03	3
284	95	=
285	35	1/X
286	65	×
287	43	RCL
288	15	15
289	95	=
290	85	+
291	93	.
292	09	9
293	09	9
294	09	9
295	95	=
296	59	INT
297	32	X:T
298	03	3
299	07	7
300	04	4
301	03	3
302	03	3
303	02	2
304	01	1
305	05	5
306	69	OP
307	04	04
308	32	X:T
309	69	OP

Print T_{woc}

Step	Code	Key
310	06	06
311	43	RCL
312	29	29
313	65	×

Constant b

Step	Code	Key
314	04	4
315	93	.
316	05	5
317	08	8
318	95	=
319	35	1/X
320	65	×
321	43	RCL
322	15	15
323	95	=
324	85	+
325	93	.
326	09	9
327	09	9
328	09	9
329	95	=
330	59	INT
331	32	X:T
332	69	OP
333	00	00
334	03	3
335	07	7
336	04	4
337	03	3
338	01	1
339	05	5
340	69	OP
341	04	04
342	32	X:T
343	69	OP

Print T_{wc}

Step	Code	Key
344	06	06
345	98	ADV
346	91	R/S
347	76	LBL
348	15	E

Readjust h_a

Step	Code	Key
349	43	RCL
350	28	28
351	42	STO
352	10	10
353	61	GTO
354	12	B
355	91	R/S
356	76	LBL
357	10	E'

Print data registers

Step	Code	Key
358	00	0
359	22	INV
360	90	LST
361	91	R/S

End program

reduces run time. After a program run, intermediate results are maintained in unused Storage Registers 11 through 29. See Table III for all stored information.

In this program, the combined convection and radiation heat-transfer coefficients are corrected by a wind factor to calculate h_a. If designing for zero wind conditions, enter 1.0 in Storage Register 23, 0 in Storage Registers 24 and 25, and run the program as usual.

Thermal conductance values, a and b, used in this program are for ½-in. tracer lines. The user may substi-

Nomenclature

A, B, C	Constants for wind-factor equation
a	Thermal conductance, tracer to pipe, without heat-transfer cement, Btu/(h)(°F)(ft of pipe)
b	Thermal conductance, tracer to pipe, with cement, Btu/(h)(°F)(ft of pipe)
C_p	Specific heat of hot medium, Btu/(lb)(°F)
d_i	Inside diameter of insulation, in.
d_o	Outside diameter of insulation, in.
h_a	Film heat-transfer coefficient to air (corrected for wind), Btu/(h)(°F)(ft²)
$h_c + h_r$	Combined convection and radiation heat-transfer coefficient, Btu/(h)(°F)(ft²)
K_i	Thermal conductivity of insulation, Btu/(h)(ft²)(°F/ft)
L_L	Total pipeline length, ft
Q	Heat lost per ft of pipe, Btu/(h)(ft)
Q_t	Total heat lost from pipeline, Btu/h
T_a	Average temperature of pipe and tracer, °F
T_{air}	Air temperature, °F
$T_{med.avg.}$	Average temperature of hot medium, °F
T_{mi}	Inlet temperature of hot medium, °F
T_{mo}	Outlet temperature of hot medium, °F
T_p	Temperature in pipe, °F
T_s	Outside surface temperature of insulation, °F
T_{wc}	Number of tracers required with heat-transfer cement
T_{woc}	Number of tracers required without heat-transfer cement
W	Flowrate of hot medium, lb/h
W_F	Wind factor

User instructions   Table II

Step	Procedure	Enter	Press	Display
1.	Read in both magnetic cards, Sides 1, 2 and 4		CLR	1, 2, 4
2.	Store data in registers R0 through R10	$R0 = L_L$		Data
		$R1 = T_p$		
		$R2 = T_{mi}$		
		$R3 = T_{mo}$		
		$R4 = T_{air}$		
		$R5 =$ Pipe O.D.		
		$R6 =$ Tracer allowance		
		$R7 = T_k$		
		$R8 = K_i$		
		$R9 = C_p$		
		$R10 = h_a$ (est.)		
3.	Press A to begin computations		A	T_{wc}
4.	Option: Press E' for printout of data registers		E'	0

Contents of data registers   Table III

0. Line length, ft
1. T_p, °F
2. T_{mi}, °F
3. T_{mo}, °F
4. T_{air}, °F
5. Pipe O.D., in.
6. Tracer allowance, in.
7. T_k, in.
8. K_i, Btu/(h)(ft²)(°F/ft)
9. C_p, Btu/(lb)(°F)
10. h_a (trial calculation, Btu/(h)(°F)(ft²)
11. d_o, in.
12. d_i, in.
13. $T_{avg.\ inside}$, °F
14. T_s, °F
15. Q, Btu/(h)(ft)
16. X
17. W, lb/h
18. 2724311700*
19. 3735131517*
20. 3500332230*
21. $T_{med.\ avg.}$, °F
22. $h_c + h_r$, Btu/(h)(°F)(ft²)
23. 2.814*
24. −0.0003885714*
25. −0.0000012857*
26. W_F
27. $T_s − T_{air}$, °F
28. h'_a, Btu/(h)(°F)(ft²)
29. $T_{med.\ avg.} − T_p$, °F

*Constants that must be stored on magnetic card before program execution (first time only).

tute constants for other-sized tracers, as given in Table IV. Constant a occupies Program Steps 280 through 283, and b occupies Steps 314 through 317. Constants for other-sized tracer lines may be keyed into the same area of the program.

An example

Estimate the number of tracers required to maintain 100 ft of 6-in.-dia. process line at 500°F. Hot tracing medium is available at 625°F, and has a heat capacity of 0.53 Btu/(lb)(°F). The process line is covered with 2.5 in. of insulation whose thermal conductivity is 0.037 Btu/(h)(ft²)(°F/ft). Design this system for 0°F air tem-

Thermal conductance values for tracer lines   Table IV

Tube size, in.	Constant, a	Constant, b
3/8	0.295	3.44
1/2	0.393	4.58
5/8	0.490	5.73

See Eq. (7) and (8)

User-defined keys   Table V

A – Starts program

B – Calculates T_s (internal)

C – Calculates $h_c + h_r$ (internal)

D – Calculates Q, Q_t, W, and number of tracers (internal)

E – Readjusts h_a for new trial (internal)

E' – Prints data registers

perature and 20-mph winds. The tracing medium is to be returned at 550°F. Use ½-in. tracers.

Enter the problem variables into the calculator:

Variable	Register	Variable	Register
$L_L = 100$	(R0)	Tracer	
$T_p = 500$	(R1)	allowance* = 1.25	(R6)
$T_{mi} = 625$	(R2)	$T_k = 2.5$	(R7)
$T_{mo} = 550$	(R3)	$K_i = 0.037$	(R8)
$T_{air} = 0$	(R4)	$C_p = 0.53$	(R9)
Pipe O.D. = 6.065	(R5)	h_a (trial) = 4.0	(R10)

Press Key A to run the program. The results print as:

```
LINE TRACER PGM
  18.84804484        TS
 234.8519058         Q
23485.19058        BTUH
 590.8224045        LB/H
          7.        TWOC
          1.        TWC
```

The estimated number of tracers without the heat-transfer cement for this example is seven, while using a heat-transfer cement reduces the required number to one. Circulation rate of the tracing medium is 590.8 lb/h, and heat lost from 100 ft of pipeline is 23,485 Btu/h.

Users not having a printer may recall most of the calculated results from the data registers (see Table III). The value displayed after program execution is T_{wc}.

For HP-67/97 users

The HP version closely follows the TI program. Table VI offers the HP program listing, and Table VII provides user instructions for the HP version. Table VIII lists the contents of the HP data registers.

*Allow approximately 1¼ in. between the pipe and insulation to accommodate the ½-in. tracer line and heat-transfer cement. For three, or more, tracers, allow twice this value. Smaller tracers may require only ⅞ to 1 in. of space. Tracers are normally spaced equidistant around the pipe (see illustration), and are run parallel to the pipe. A final run with the calculator program may be made after the total number of tracers and spacing has been established.

Program listing for HP version

Table VI

Step	Key	Code	Step	Key	Code	Step	Key	Code	Step	Key	Code	Step	Key	Code	Step	Key	Code
001	*LBLA	21 11	040	2	02	079	STOE	35 15	118	2	02	157	9	09			
002	P≷S	16-51	041	÷	-24	080	RCL4	36 04	119	÷	-24	158	9	09			
003	RCL2	36 02	042	2	02	081	P≷S	16-51	120	RCL4	36 04	159	÷	-55			
004	RCL3	36 03	043	÷	-24	082	RCL4	36 04	121	P≷S	16-51	160	INT	16 34			
005	+	-55	044	P≷S	16-51	083	-	-45	122	RCL4	36 04	161	DSP0	-63 00			
006	2	02	045	RCL8	36 08	084	STOB	35 12	123	-	-45	162	PRTX	-14			
007	÷	-24	046	÷	-24	085	P≷S	16-51	124	x	-35	163	RCL2	36 02			
008	P≷S	16-51	047	STOD	35 14	086	RCL7	36 07	125	P≷S	16-51	164	4	04			
009	STO6	35 06	048	RCL4	36 04	087	STO0	35 00	126	STO5	35 05	165	.	-62			
010	P≷S	16-51	049	x	-35	088	RCLB	36 12	127	PRTX	-14	166	5	05			
011	RCL1	36 01	050	P≷S	16-51	089	RCL8	36 08	128	P≷S	16-51	167	8	08			
012	+	-55	051	RCL3	36 03	090	x	-35	129	RCL0	36 00	168	x	-35			
013	2	02	052	+	-55	091	ST+0	35-55 00	130	x	-35	169	1/X	52			
014	÷	-24	053	RCLD	36 14	092	RCLE	36 12	131	PRTX	-14	170	RCL5	36 05			
015	P≷S	16-51	054	1	01	093	X²	53	132	RCL9	36 09	171	x	-35			
016	STO3	35 03	055	+	-55	094	RCL9	36 09	133	÷	-24	172	.	-62			
017	P≷S	16-51	056	÷	-24	095	x	-35	134	RCL2	36 02	173	9	09			
018	RCL5	36 05	057	STO4	35 04	096	ST+0	35-55 00	135	RCL3	36 03	174	9	09			
019	RCL6	36 06	058	*LBLC	21 13	097	RCL0	36 00	136	-	-45	175	9	09			
020	+	-55	059	RCL1	36 01	098	RCLE	36 15	137	÷	-24	176	+	-55			
021	P≷S	16-51	060	.	-62	099	x	-35	138	PRTX	-14	177	INT	16 34			
022	STO2	35 02	061	1	01	100	STOC	35 13	139	STOI	35 46	178	PRTX	-14			
023	P≷S	16-51	062	9	09	101	RCLA	36 11	140	P≷S	16-51	179	DSP2	-63 02			
024	RCL7	36 07	063	Y^x	31	102	-	-45	141	RCL6	36 06	180	R/S	51			
025	2	02	064	2	02	103	ABS	16 31	142	P≷S	16-51	181	*LBLE	21 15			
026	x	-35	065	7	07	104	.	-62	143	RCL1	36 01	182	RCLC	36 13			
027	+	-55	066	3	03	105	0	00	144	-	-45	183	STOA	35 11			
028	P≷S	16-51	067	RCL4	36 04	106	1	01	145	STOB	35 12	184	GTOB	22 12			
029	STO1	35 01	068	P≷S	16-51	107	X≤Y?	16-35	146	.	-62	185	R/S	51			
030	*LBLB	21 12	069	RCL4	36 04	108	GTOE	22 15	147	3	03	186	*LBLe	21 16 15			
031	RCL1	36 01	070	-	-45	109	*LBLD	21 14	148	9	09	187	DSP9	-63 09			
032	RCL2	36 02	071	-	-45	110	RCL4	36 04	149	3	03	188	FREG	16-13			
033	÷	-24	072	x	-35	111	PRTX	-14	150	x	-35	189	DSP2	-63 02			
034	LN	32	073	1/X	52	112	RCLC	36 13	151	1/X	52	190	RTN	24			
035	RCLA	36 11	074	5	05	113	Pi	16-24	152	P≷S	16-51	191	R/S	51			
036	x	-35	075	6	06	114	x	-35	153	RCL5	36 05						
037	RCL1	36 01	076	4	04	115	RCL1	36 01	154	x	-35						
038	x	-35	077	x	-35	116	x	-35	155	.	-62						
039	1	01	078	P≷S	16-51	117	1	01	156	9	09						

User instructions for HP version

Table VII

Store the following data:

Pipeline length, ft	L_L	STO 0
Temperature in pipe, °F	T_p	STO 1
Inlet temperature, hot medium, °F	T_{mi}	STO 2
Outlet temperature, hot medium, °F	T_{mo}	STO 3
Air temperature, °F	T_{air}	STO 4
Pipe OD, in.		STO 5
Tracer allowance, in.		STO 6
Insulation thickness, in.	T_k	STO 7
Thermal conductivity of insulation, Btu/(h)(ft²)(°F/ft)	K_i	STO 8
Heat capacity of hot medium, Btu/(lb)(°F)	C_p	STO 9
Air film coefficient, estimate, Btu/(h)(°F)(ft²)	h_a	STO A

Exchange registers   P ⇌ S

Store constants:	2.814	STO 7
(See note below)	−3.885712E−4	STO 8
	−1.285E-6	STO 9

Run program with key **A**

Section IV
Condensers

Fog formation in low-temperature condensers

A sulfuric acid mist that might corrode through process piping is an example of a dangerous fog. The following information on predicting and combating fog in low-temperature condensers could prevent a lot of trouble.

Lidia LoPinto, Consultant

☐ When low-temperature condensers are used to recover small concentrations of vapor in a stream of noncondensables, fogging can occur. A fog is a suspension of fine droplets, ranging from less than 1 micron up to 10 microns in diameter. A fog this fine is difficult to capture with conventional equipment such as mist eliminators. If the fog is an aerosol having a corrosive or reactive condensate, it might eventually settle and create corrosion problems downstream.

Fogging is not often reported as a problem because it is seldom looked for. Its presence becomes known only when yield losses, or pollution or corrosion problems become apparent.

A fog can be formed in a condenser when the ratio of noncondensable to condensable vapor is high and the temperature differential is high. One example is in the recovery of trace solvents from effluent gases, using refrigerated condensers for air-pollution-control purposes. Under these conditions, the heat-transfer rate is much greater than the mass-transfer rate, so that the vapor undergoes "quick chilling" and condenses midstream before reaching the condenser wall. A fog will probably form, depending on whether or not nuclei of condensation are available.

When does fog become visible?

Supersaturation is measured by the ratio of the actual vapor pressure of the condensable vapor to the equilibrium vapor pressure at the given temperature:

$$S = \frac{P}{P_{\infty(T)}} \qquad (1)$$

where S = supersaturation ratio; P = vapor pressure, mm Hg; and $P_{\infty(T)}$ = equilibrium vapor pressure at temperature T.

Before fog can become visible by the light-scattering test (Tyndall effect), the mixture will reach a certain level of supersaturation. The level at which a visible fog occurs is called the critical supersaturation ratio, S_{cr}. This value is characteristic of the particular vapor and

Typical values of critical supersaturation ratio

	T, K	S_{cr}
Methyl alcohol	270.0	3.20 ± 0.10
Ethyl alcohol	273.2	2.30 ± 0.05
n-Propyl alcohol	270.4	3.05 ± 0.05
Nitromethane	252.2	6.05 ± 0.75
Water	263.7	4.85 ± 0.08

Source: Ref 3, p. 18.

noncondensable mixture, and varies with temperature. Some typical values, measured by cloud-chamber technique, are shown in Table I.

These values correspond to fairly clean gases. If dusts or other nuclei are present, S_{cr} approaches 1.

S_{cr} can be estimated using Fenhel's formula in [1]:

$$S_{cr} = \mathrm{Exp}\left[84\frac{M}{\rho_L}\left(\frac{\sigma}{T}\right)^{1.5}\right] \qquad (2)$$

where σ = surface tension, dynes/cm
ρ_L = liquid density, lb/ft^3
T = temperature, degrees Rankine
M = molecular weight of condensable

S_{cr} can be measured by experimental means. Note that it decreases with temperature.

For practical purposes, it is sufficient to assume that fog will be formed when $S \geq 1$ [2]. If free gaseous ions exist in the gas, and the droplets become charged, fogging may occur even when $S < 1$. This is discussed in Ref. 3.

Estimating supersaturation

If we calculate the maximum value of S that will occur in a system, we can see whether this is large enough to cause fogging.

A formula for the calculation of S for condensation in

Originally published May 17, 1982

a tube is derived by Amelin [3] from differential heat- and mass-transfer formulas:

$$S = \left(\frac{T - T_2}{T_1 - T_2}\right)^{K\delta}\left(\frac{P_1 - P_2}{P_{\infty(T)}}\right) + \frac{P_2}{P_{\infty(T)}} \quad (3)$$

where T = temperature at any point in the condenser tube (use consistent units, K or °R)

T_1 = initial gas temperature

T_2 = temperature of the condensation surface

P_1 = vapor pressure of condensable at initial temperature T_1 (use consistent absolute units)

P_2 = vapor pressure of condensable at wall temperature T_2

$P_{\infty(T)}$ = equilibrium vapor pressure at T

$$K = 1 + \left(\frac{P - P_\eta}{P - P_2}\right)\left(\frac{F_n}{F_w}\right) \quad (4)$$

where, as defined in Ref. 3, p. 107:

P = vapor pressure at T

P_η = saturated vapor pressure at the temperature of the nuclei (corrected for droplet curvature). Assume it is equal to $P_{\infty(T)}$ for initial estimate.

F_n = surface area of nuclei/unit pipe length

F_w = surface area of pipe/unit pipe length

$$\delta = \left(\frac{C\rho K_D}{K_T}\right)^m \quad (5)$$

(from Ref. 3, p. 106)

where C = heat capacity of gas, Btu/lb°F

ρ = density of gas, lb/ft^3

K_D = diffusivity of vapor in condensable, ft/h (see box)

K_T = thermal conductivity, Btu/(min) (ft^2) (°F/ft)

and m = a dimensionless index, 0.6 for turbulent flow, 0.7 for laminar flow

Function $S = f(T)$ has a maximum. By calculating S at the maximum, we can see whether fogging occurs, without calculating the whole supersaturation curve, because if fogging occurs at all, it will occur at S_{max}.

To determine S_{max}, $P_{\infty(T)}$ is replaced by the expression:

$$P_{\infty(T)} = e^{C - E/T} \quad (6)$$

(from Ref. 3, p. 2)

where $E = Q/1.987$

and Q = molar heat of vaporization, Btu/lb mole

$S = f(T)$ is differentiated and set equal to 0. P_2 is eliminated, as it is generally negligible compared with P_1. This yields an expression for T_{max} (the temperature at S_{max}):

$$T_{max} = \frac{E \pm \sqrt{E^2 - 4\delta E T_2 K}}{2K\delta} \quad (7)$$

if we take the positive root (see Ref. 3, p. 102).

T_{max} is then substituted into the supersaturation expression $S = f(T)$ to obtain S_{max}. If $S_{max} > 1$, then fogging is probably occurring. The fogging will not be visible unless $S_{max} > S_{cr}$, by definition.

Cures for fogging

■ **Reduce ΔT and increase A**—If the temperature differential across the tubes is reduced, and the surface

---

Gas diffusivity

K_D data are generally scarce. Perry's Handbook, Section 14 [1], contains good methods for estimating gas diffusivity. One way to measure the ratio of K_D to K_T is by taking the wet- and dry-bulb temperatures and employing the formula:

$$\lambda(H_s - H) = \frac{hc}{K_G}(T - T_W)$$

where λ = latent heat of vaporization, Btu/lb

H_s = equilibrium concentration of vapor at temperature T, lb/lb of dry gas

H = actual concentration of vapor, lb/lb dry gas

T = dry-bulb temperature, °F

T_W = wet-bulb temperature, °F

hc = film heat-transfer coefficient, Btu/(lb) (°F) (ft^2)

K_G = mass transfer coefficient, lb/(h)(ft^2)(atm)

and $\dfrac{hc}{K_G} = C\left(\dfrac{K_T}{C\rho K_D}\right)^{2/3}$

---

area is increased, the heat flow remains similar, but the driving force for heat transfer is decreased, and the ratio of mass transfer to heat transfer is increased. This "gradual cooling" approach is the most conventional cure cited in various references.

It can be expensive, however. These exchangers will often be handling very corrosive substances and will require exotic materials of construction. In one such design I handled, the condenser tubes were specified to be Hastelloy. When enough area was added to prevent fogging, the price of the condenser nearly doubled.

■ **Use a mist eliminator**—There are some high-performance mist eliminators on the market that can remove particles in the "fogging" range. However, these units require large areas and high pressure drops. Again, costs can soar if exotic materials of construction are specified. If this solution is sought, I recommend that the equipment should be thoroughly tested on a bench scale.

■ **Seed the gas stream with condensation nuclei**—To produce drops that can be captured with a conventional mist eliminator or settler. This is a less-conventional approach (Ref. 3, p. 107), but it is probably less costly than other methods. Testing is recommended to ensure that the scheme will work for the particular chemicals and prevailing conditions.

■ **Filter the gases**—Almost all industrial gases will carry mists and dusts that will provide nuclei for fog condensation. The greater the concentration of these dusts, the lower the value of S_{cr}. Qualitative experimental observations were done by Amelin to confirm this. Fog may in some cases be inhibited by filtration of the gases prior to condensation. A clue to the existence of a dust problem is when a fog is reported but the supersaturation expression yields values of less than the calculated value of S_{cr}.

■ **Other methods**—Some somewhat-less-practical solutions are discussed in the literature. One presents a method of inhibiting fog formation by stringing a heated wire across the center of the exchanger tube. An electrical current will provide the heat.

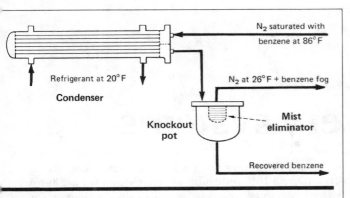

Fog reduces efficiency of benzene recovery   **Fig. 1**

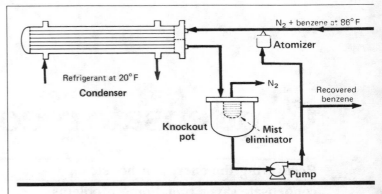

Fogging is reduced by seeding with benzene mist   **Fig. 2**

Benzene fog in a nitrogen stream

A benzene-recovery condenser is designed to knock down 83% of the benzene from a nitrogen stream (see Fig. 1). Nitrogen saturated with benzene enters the tube bundle at 86°F and exits at 26°F. The refrigerant temperature is 20°F. Check to see whether fogging is a problem, and propose a solution. The pressure is 1 atm, the tubes are 1 in., and the gas velocity through the tubes is 30 ft/s.

A vapor-pressure expression for benzene is correlated from data in Perry [1]:

$$\log P = 6.89272 - 1203.53/(219.8 + t)$$

where t = °C, P = mm Hg (absolute)

$T_1 = 86°F$, $P_{\infty(T_1)} = 119$ mm Hg = P_1
$T_2 = 20°F$, $P_{\infty(T_2)} = 17$ mm Hg = P_2
$T_{av} = 56°F$, $P_{\infty(T_{av})} = 53$ mm Hg

Average molecular weight, $M = 32$
Gas density from ideal gas law = 0.085 lb/ft³ = ρ
Thermal conductivity of N_2 = 0.009 Btu/(h)(ft²) (°F/ft) = K_T
Diffusivity of benzene in N_2 = 0.0104 cm²/s or 0.0402 ft²/h = K_D

(above value from Gilliland equation, in Perry, Section 14.0 [1].

Eq. 5 yields:

$$\delta = \frac{C\rho K_D^{0.6}}{K_T} = 0.243, \text{ (turbulent flow)}$$

Eq. 7 yields:

$$T_{max} = \frac{E \pm \sqrt{E^2 - 4\delta E T_2 K}}{2K\delta}$$

where $K = 1.0$ (no nuclei being introduced)
$E = Q/1.987$
Q for benezene = 14,430 Btu/lb mole
= 7,262 °R^{-1}

$T_{max} = 488°R$ or $28°F$

$$S_{max} = \left(\frac{T_{max} - T_2}{T_1 - T_2}\right)^\delta \frac{(P_1 - P_2)}{P_{\infty T_{max}}} + \frac{P_2}{P_{\infty T_{max}}}$$

$$S_{max} = \left(\frac{28 - 26}{86 - 26}\right)^{0.243}\left(\frac{119 - 17}{23}\right) + \frac{17}{23}$$

$$S_{max} = 2.67$$

Therefore, fogging is occurring, since $S_{max} > 1.0$.

A simple and effective solution is obtained by recycling some of the recovered benzene through an atomizer to provide condensation nuclei so that large, recoverable droplets are formed (see Fig. 2).

To find the value of K, select a value of $S_{max} \leq 1$ and substitute in Eq. 4:

$$K = 1 + \left(\frac{2.67(23) - 23}{2.67(23) - 17}\right)\left(\frac{F_n}{F_w}\right) = 2.45$$

P_η should be determined experimentally from Eq. 4, but, in this case, we can approximate $P_\eta = P_{\infty T_{max}}$.
Hence $F_n/F_w = 1.67$.

For a 1-in. tube, $F_w = 0.26$ ft²/ft; therefore, $F_n = 0.43$ ft²/ft. The total area of nuclei/s to be provided = 0.43 ft²/ft × 30 ft/s = 12.9 ft²/s. Assuming spherical droplets 100µ in diameter are produced by an atomizer nozzle, the flowrate of liquid benzene to be injected into the incoming stream is 0.3 gpm.

It can be seen that the equations for predicting fogging in pipes under turbulent and laminar flow, as derived by Amelin, can be applied to practical condenser design for preliminary calculations. Testing is recommended for final design.

References

1. Perry, Robert H. and Chilton, Cecil H., "Chemical Engineers' Handbook," fifth ed., McGraw-Hill, New York.
2. Branan, C., "The Process Engineer's Pocket Handbook," 1978, Gulf Pub. Co., P.O. Box 2608, Houston, TX 77001.
3. Amelin, A. G., "Theory of Fog Condensation," 1967, Daniel Davey and Co., Inc., P.O. Box 6088, Hartford, CT 06106.

The author

Lidia Llamas LoPinto is a technical writing consultant specializing in process operating manuals and software documentation, 41 Travers Ave., New York, NY 10705, tel: 914-963-3695. She has worked in process-design and environmental and safety departments in a variety of assignments for Stauffer Chemical Co., Chemical Air Pollution Control Co. and American Cyanamid Co. She holds an M.Ch.E. and B.Ch.E. from Manhattan College. She is an Engineer in Training, a member of the Soc. of Women Engineers and an Industrial Advisor for the Junior Engineering Technical Soc.

Listing for TI version—program B

Table V

Step	Code	Key	Step	Code	Key	Step	Code	Key	Step	Code	Key	Step	Code	Key
000	76	LBL	056	21	21	111	75	-	166	77	GE	221	35	35
001	11	A	057	42	STO	112	53	(	167	33	X²	222	22	INV
002	43	RCL	058	02	02	113	73	RC*	168	76	LBL	223	87	IFF
003	17	17	059	43	RCL	114	25	25	169	32	X:T	224	02	02
004	85	+	060	08	08	115	65	×	170	43	RCL	225	35	1/X
005	43	RCL	061	75	-	116	43	RCL	171	24	24	226	43	RCL
006	18	18	062	53	(	117	24	24	172	99	PRT	227	35	35
007	85	+	063	43	RCL	118	54	)	173	43	RCL	228	42	STO
008	43	RCL	064	11	11	119	95	=	174	23	23	229	22	22
009	19	19	065	65	×	120	42	STO	175	99	PRT	230	22	INV
010	95	=	066	43	RCL	121	04	04	176	43	RCL	231	86	STF
011	42	STO	067	24	24	122	71	SBR	177	22	22	232	02	02
012	20	20	068	54	)	123	23	LNX	178	99	PRT	233	76	LBL
013	43	RCL	069	95	=	124	01	1	179	43	RCL	234	35	1/X
014	08	08	070	42	STO	125	44	SUM	180	21	21	235	73	RC*
015	42	STO	071	04	04	126	25	25	181	99	PRT	236	25	25
016	03	03	072	71	SBR	127	43	RCL	182	91	R/S	237	55	÷
017	53	(	073	23	LNX	128	02	02	183	76	LBL	238	43	RCL
018	43	RCL	074	86	STF	129	42	STO	184	23	LNX	239	35	35
019	08	08	075	02	02	130	01	01	185	43	RCL	240	85	+
020	75	-	076	43	RCL	131	43	RCL	186	01	01	241	43	RCL
021	43	RCL	077	21	21	132	01	01	187	75	-	242	10	10
022	07	07	078	42	STO	133	75	-	188	43	RCL	243	95	=
023	54	)	079	01	01	134	43	RCL	189	04	04	244	42	STO
024	55	÷	080	01	1	135	23	23	190	95	=	245	10	10
025	43	RCL	081	02	2	136	95	=	191	42	STO	246	92	RTN
026	20	20	082	42	STO	137	42	STO	192	00	00	247	76	LBL
027	95	=	083	25	25	138	02	02	193	43	RCL	248	33	X²
028	42	STO	084	61	GTO	139	43	RCL	194	02	02	249	53	(
029	24	24	085	24	CE	140	04	04	195	75	-	250	53	(
030	01	1	086	76	LBL	141	42	STO	196	43	RCL	251	43	RCL
031	01	1	087	22	INV	142	03	03	197	03	03	252	20	20
032	42	STO	088	43	RCL	143	43	RCL	198	95	=	253	75	-
033	25	25	089	05	05	144	25	25	199	42	STO	254	43	RCL
034	43	RCL	090	42	STO	145	32	X:T	200	09	09	255	11	11
035	23	23	091	01	01	146	01	1	201	53	(	256	54	)
036	65	×	092	01	1	147	06	6	202	43	RCL	257	55	÷
037	05	5	093	02	2	148	77	GE	203	00	00	258	53	(
038	85	+	094	42	STO	149	24	CE	204	75	-	259	43	RCL
039	43	RCL	095	25	25	150	43	RCL	205	43	RCL	260	10	10
040	06	06	096	00	0	151	20	20	206	09	09	261	75	-
041	95	=	097	42	STO	152	55	÷	207	54	)	262	53	(
042	42	STO	098	22	'22	153	43	RCL	208	55	÷	263	43	RCL
043	21	21	099	76	LBL	154	10	10	209	53	(	264	11	11
044	43	RCL	100	24	CE	155	95	=	210	53	(	265	55	÷
045	05	05	101	43	RCL	156	42	STO	211	43	RCL	266	43	RCL
046	32	X:T	102	01	01	157	24	24	212	00	00	267	22	22
047	43	RCL	103	75	-	158	42	STO	213	55	÷	268	54	)
048	21	21	104	43	RCL	159	23	23	214	43	RCL	269	54	)
049	77	GE	105	23	23	160	00	0	215	09	09	270	54	)
050	22	INV	106	95	=	161	32	X:T	216	54	)	271	95	=
051	43	RCL	107	42	STO	162	43	RCL	217	23	LNX	272	42	STO
052	05	05	108	02	02	163	11	11	218	54	)	273	23	23
053	42	STO	109	43	RCL	164	67	EQ	219	95	=	274	61	GTO
054	01	01	110	03	03	165	32	X:T	220	42	STO	275	32	X:T
055	43	RCL												

Superheated vapor condensation in heat exchanger design

Some exchanger transfer surface will be dry if the entering superheated vapor is hot enough. However, accounting properly for this dry-wall heat transfer could actually result in smaller surface area, and less-expensive tube material.

D. H. Foxall and *H. R. Chappell, IMI Yorkshire Imperial Ltd.*

☐ Condensation heat transfer from pure saturated vapors is well understood and usually can be evaluated accurately.

If the vapor is superheated at the heat exchanger inlet, the heat flux might be only marginally increased. In such a case there will be little error in evaluating the duty as if the vapor were saturated, except for also taking into account the additional sensible heat that must be transferred.

If, however, the superheat temperature is sufficiently high that some of the heat-transfer surface will be dry, the saturated-vapor assumption may not be satisfactory. This problem is not always dealt with suitably in heat-exchanger design, there being at least the following two incorrect assumptions that may be made:

1. A high superheat temperature must be accompanied by a high tube-wall temperature. If the duty is accurately evaluated, however, it may be found that a tube material that was thought unacceptable based on temperature considerations would actually be satisfactory. Such a situation may arise with steam-heated calorifiers, for which copper alloy tubes have sometimes been specified when copper could have been used. In duties in which condensation begins after the vapor has lost some of its superheat, the tube surface temperature is higher in the dry than in the wet region, but the difference may not be substantial.

2. Heat transfer in the dry-wall region will be so poor as to require a disproportionately large surface area. However, because the dry-wall heat flux is greater than the saturation flux, taking this factor into account may make it possible to reduce heat-exchange surface area significantly. This may be the case with, for example, hydrocarbon condensers, in which the mass velocity

Originally published December 29, 1980

Nomenclature

A Surface area per unit length of tube, ft²/ft
- A_c Coolant side
- A_v Vapor side
- A_w Effective mean-wall-area

h Film heat-transfer coefficient, Btu/(h)(ft²)(°F)
- h_c Across cooling-fluid boundary layer
- h_L Saturated-vapor condensing coefficient
- h_v Across vapor boundary layer (h_t at the transition temperature, T_t)
- h_s Superheated-vapor true condensing coefficient
- h_{sv} Superheated-vapor apparent condensing coefficient (allowing for sensible heat transferred)

K_w Thermal conductivity of tube wall, Btu/(h)(ft²)(°F)/ft

L Length of tube, ft

q Rate of heat transfer, Btu/h

r Fouling factor, (h)(ft²)(°F)/Btu
- r_c Cooling fluid
- r_v Condensing fluid

T Temperature, °F
- T_c Cooling fluid
- T_L Saturated vapor
- T_v Superheated vapor (T_i vapor inlet, T_t at onset of condensation)

T_b At vapor-surface interface (estimated from dry wall calculation, $T_b = T_v - \Delta T_v = T_c + \Delta T_{ov} - \Delta T_v$)

U Overall heat-transfer coefficient (related to vapor-side surface area), Btu/(h)(ft²)(°F)

U' Partial overall coefficient, excluding resistances across vapor boundary layer and condensate film
- U_L, U'_L With saturated vapor
- U_v, U'_v Superheated vapor, dry wall (U_t, U'_t at the transition temperature, T_t)
- U_s, U'_s Superheated vapor, wet wall; note that definition of U_s, Eq. (7) and (8), excludes resistance across vapor boundary layer

x Tube wall thickness, ft

α $[h_s T_s / h_L T_L]^{1/3}$

ΔT Temperature difference, °F
- ΔT_c Across cooling-fluid boundary layer
- ΔT_L Across condensate film (saturated vapor)
- ΔT_s Across condensate film (superheated vapor)
- ΔT_v Across vapor boundary layer
- ΔT_{oL} Temperature difference between saturated vapor and cooling fluid ($T_L - T_c$)
- ΔT_{ov} Temperature difference between superheated vapor and cooling fluid ($T_v - T_c$)

may be high, and the condensing coefficient much lower than for steam.

Outlined in this article is a procedure for estimating the effect of superheat. Calculated first is the saturated-vapor heat transfer; next, the heat transfer at the vapor inlet temperature, assuming that no condensation takes place—which result establishes whether a dry region will actually occur.

If it is found that the surface will be dry at the inlet temperature, another calculation will determine the transition vapor temperature, T_t, below which condensation will occur, so that the dry and wet surface portions of the duty can be distinguished. As the vapor is cooled from T_t to T_L (the saturated vapor temperature), the mean flux remains higher than the saturation flux.

A method will be given in this article for estimating the flux in this superheated-vapor-to-wet-surface range. The procedure can be applied to any type of duty for which saturated-vapor and dry-wall calculations can be carried out. It is first illustrated by a simple example and later by more-complex but perhaps more-realistic calculations.

Reference to flux (heat transfer per unit surface area) in all cases relates to the vapor-side surface area. Flux at the coolant surface is in general different because, while the total amount of heat flowing is the same, the amount of surface area is not. The difference in flux at the two surfaces is substantial if the tube is finned.

The overall heat-transfer coefficient, U, is also defined so that it relates to the vapor-side surface (whether this is internal or external). This involves a minor difference from the usual convention of relating U always to the same surface (most frequently, the external surface).

Saturated-vapor coefficient defined

With the foregoing definition of U, the general form of equation for heat transfer with saturated vapor can be written:

$$\frac{1}{U_L} = \left(\frac{1}{h_c}\right)\left(\frac{A_v}{A_c}\right) + r_c\left(\frac{A_v}{A_c}\right) + \left(\frac{x}{K_w}\right)\left(\frac{A_v}{A_w}\right) + r_v + \frac{1}{h_L} \quad (1)$$

The analysis that follows later can be more easily presented if a partial overall heat-transfer coefficient (U' in general, or U'_L for saturated vapor) is defined. In this article, U' is defined as the overall coefficient that would be obtained from the resistances across the coolant boundary layer, tube wall and any fouling deposits, but excluding the resistance across the condensate film and (in the case of superheated vapor) across the vapor boundary layer.

With this definition, the overall coefficient for saturated vapor is:

$$\frac{1}{U'_L} = \left(\frac{1}{h_c}\right)\left(\frac{A_v}{A_c}\right) + r_c\left(\frac{A_v}{A_c}\right) + \left(\frac{x}{K_w}\right)\left(\frac{A_v}{A_w}\right) + r_v$$
$$= (1/U_L) - (1/h_L) \quad (1a)$$

Perhaps the first to use this type of approach were Colburn and Hougen in dealing with condensation from a mixture containing noncondensable gas [1].

However, they excluded only the resistance across the vapor boundary layer, having included the condensate film resistance in the determination of U'.

The overall temperature difference (ΔT_{oL}, in the case of saturated vapor) is distributed across the individual resistances in proportion to their magnitudes. The main concern here is to separate ΔT_{oL} into ΔT_L (across the condensate film) and into $\Delta T_{oL} - \Delta T_L$ (which is distributed across the other resistances).

Considering continuity of heat flow:

$$U_L \Delta T_{oL} = U'_L (\Delta T_{oL} - \Delta T_L) = h_L \Delta T_L \quad (2)$$

Any of these expressions gives the flux at the condensing surface.

Heat transfer per unit length of tube is obtained by multiplying this flux by A_v, the vapor-side surface area per unit length:

$$U_L A_v \Delta T_{oL} = U'_L A_v (\Delta T_{oL} - \Delta T_L) = h_L A_v \Delta T_L \quad (3)$$

Superheated vapor with dry wall

The means for the determination of heat transfer is provided by the fundamental Eq. (1), but it is suggested that the subscript L in the terms be changed to v to emphasize that the vapor-side heat-transfer mechanism is different:

$$\frac{1}{U_v} = \left(\frac{1}{h_c}\right)\left(\frac{A_v}{A_c}\right) + r_c\left(\frac{A_v}{A_c}\right) + \left(\frac{x}{K_w}\right)\left(\frac{A_v}{A_w}\right) + r_v + \frac{1}{h_v} \quad (4)$$

The overall temperature difference, ΔT_{ov}, which is greater than the saturation temperature difference, ΔT_{oL}, is also changed.

With the definition of partial overall coefficient already given:

$$\frac{1}{U'_v} = \left(\frac{1}{h_c}\right)\left(\frac{A_v}{A_c}\right) + r_c\left(\frac{A_v}{A_c}\right) + \left(\frac{x}{K_w}\right)\left(\frac{A_v}{A_w}\right) + r_v \quad (4a)$$
$$= (1/U_v) - (1/h_v)$$

U'_v and U'_L are determined from the same set of resistances, and in practice the difference may be negligible. However, the change in temperature may alter the value of h_c significantly between the two calculations, and U' cannot necessarily be assumed constant. The possible importance of this point will be shown in the examples that follow.

Should the surface be dry, the equation for flux corresponds to Eq. (2):

$$U_v \Delta T_{ov} = U'_v (\Delta T_{ov} - \Delta T_v) = h_v \Delta T_v \quad (5)$$

The surface is dry if its calculated temperature, T_b, is above saturation point, T_L, and it is wet if T_b is below T_L—i.e.,

Dry: $T_b > T_L$
Wet: $T_b < T_L$
But $T_b = T_c + (\Delta T_{ov} - \Delta T_v)$
And $T_L = T_c + \Delta T_{oL}$
The criterion can thus be expressed:
Dry: $\Delta T_{ov} - \Delta T_v > \Delta T_{oL}$
Wet: $\Delta T_{ov} - \Delta T_v < \Delta T_{oL}$
The solution to Eq. (4) and (5) must be examined by this criterion.

If a dry surface is confirmed, the calculation is valid and gives the correct flux and surface temperature.

A calculation that shows that the surface will be wet is correct in this respect but otherwise invalid. The flux and surface temperatures obtained should not be used in design calculations.

Before illustrating this point numerically, it is convenient to define the transition vapor temperature, T_t, at the boundary between the two regions.

It will be clear from the foregoing that when the vapor temperature is T_t:

$$T_b = T_L \text{ and } \Delta T_{ov} - \Delta T_v = \Delta T_{oL}$$

Using the subscript t to denote also the particular values of the heat-transfer coefficient obtained at vapor temperature T_t, Eq. (5) now yields:

$$U_t(T_t - T_c) = U'_t \Delta T_{oL} = h_t(T_t - T_L) \quad (5a)$$

If the vapor is sufficiently superheated at the inlet temperature for the surface to be dry, a simple calculation will then give a vapor temperature near to T_t. A second dry-wall calculation using Eq. (4) at this vapor temperature will enable T_t to be estimated accurately.

This appears to be the most appropriate point at which to illustrate the procedure with Example 1.

1: Steam condensing inside tube

This example presents the numerical procedure in its most fundamental form, without the complications usual in actual practice.

A 1-in.-dia. horizontal plain round tube is immersed in water at 200°F. Steam at atmospheric pressure flows through the tube, its velocity being 100 ft/s at its inlet temperature of 500°F. Heat transfer to the water is by natural convection.

Conditions are clean and the tube-wall thickness is assumed negligible so that its resistance, and the difference between external and internal surface areas, can be ignored.

For heat transfer at saturation temperature, Eq. (1) reduces to:

$$(1/U_L) = (1/h_c) + (1/h_L)$$

The partial overall coefficient, U'_L, simply equals the value of h_c determined at these conditions. The film coefficient h_c is based on the usual natural-convection assumptions [2] and h_L is calculated by the method recommended by Kern (i.e., calculating as for external condensation on a horizontal tube, except that the condensate loading is taken to be twice the calculated mean value) [3].

The saturated-vapor calculation provides the first entry in Table I: $U_L = 150.3$ Btu/(h)(°F)(ft²), $\Delta T_{oL} = 12$°F, and the product of U_L and $\Delta T_{oL} = 1,804$ Btu/(h)(ft²), the saturation flux.

Assuming the surface to be dry at the inlet temperature of 500°F, h_v is estimated as for a dry gas [4]. In this example, the Reynolds number (approximately 20,000) is well into the turbulent region. At the inlet temperature, $\Delta T_{ov} - \Delta T_v$ is found to be 21.35°F. As this is greater than ΔT_{oL} (12°F), it is established that the surface will be dry at the vapor inlet. The flux is therefore correctly estimated to be 3,932 Btu/(h)(ft²).

Two simple approximations are now made to find a vapor temperature near to T_t:

1. At T_t, the temperature difference associated with the partial overall coefficient is ΔT_{oL} [Eq. (5a)]. It is assumed for the moment that the variation in U' over the wet-wall range is small enough for the value U'_L already obtained to be treated as a constant. An approximation to the transition flux is then given by $U'_L \Delta T_{oL}$ [in Example 1, $155.4 \times 21 = 1,865$ Btu/(h)(ft²)].

The error in this approximate result is usually fairly small.

2. Flux in the dry-wall region is taken to be proportional to $(T_v - T_c)$, again an assumption that is accurate enough for the immediate purpose. The flux estimate from the first approximation gives a value of T_v fairly near the transition point:

$$\frac{T_v - T_c}{T_i - T_c} = \frac{\text{Approximate transition flux}}{\text{Inlet flux}} = \frac{U'_L \, \Delta T_{oL}}{U_v \, \Delta T_{ov}}$$

Here, T_i is the vapor inlet temperature. In Example 1, this gives:

$$T_v = 200 + (500 - 200)(1{,}865/3{,}932) = 342.3°F$$

The second dry-wall calculation is carried out at this temperature, which proves to be below the transition temperature, as the calculated $\Delta T_{ov} - \Delta T_v$ (11.48°F) is less than ΔT_{oL} (12°F). Although the calculation, therefore, should not be used for design purposes, it enables T_t to be estimated by interpolation.

The temperature T_t is that at which $\Delta T_{ov} - \Delta T_v = \Delta T_{oL}$. Therefore, by interpolation:

$$\frac{T_t - 342.3}{500 - 342.3} = \frac{12 - 11.48}{21.35 - 11.48}$$

This expression is given only numerically to avoid introducing additional subscripts that might cause unnecessary confusion. The procedure is obvious.

For Example 1, T_t is estimated in this way to be 350.6°F. It is unlikely that there will be a significant error in this figure; but, should there be any doubt, its accuracy can be checked by means of another dry-wall calculation.

The transition flux also can now be corrected. The procedure recommended is to interpolate for h_t between the two values of h_v already obtained [14.11 and 13.61 Btu/(h)(ft²)(°F), at $T_v = 500°F$ and 342.3°F, respectively]. From these figures, h_t (at 350.6°F) is estimated to be 13.64 Btu/(h)(ft²)(°F); and, from Eq. (5a):

Transition flux = $h_t(T_t - T_L) = 13.64 \times 138.6 = 1,891$ Btu/(h)(ft²).

Although the second dry-wall calculation proved invalid, the value of h_v obtained was the vapor-side coefficient, assuming the surface to be dry; so it is useful for obtaining h_t without a more detailed calculation. U'_t, which will be useful if the wet-wall region is to be further investigated, is obtained from Eq. (5a).

The magnitude of the error in assuming the transition flux to be equal to $U'_L \Delta T_{oL}$ is now evident. In this example, h_c, being a natural-convection coefficient, is sensitive to changes in ΔT_c and therefore varies appreciably. The error in the approximation is essentially that h_c is taken to be constant; however, as will be seen, the effect is not significant.

In many cases (as in Example 2, which follows), h_c does not vary significantly, so $U'_L \Delta T_{oL}$ represents the transition flux accurately.

In all cases, the tube wall temperature found at the vapor inlet determines the suitability, as to strength, of a material that is preferred in other respects (e.g., on corrosion-resistance grounds). If the wall is dry, it will be above saturation temperature but the excess is not usually substantial.

The effective mean flux in the dry-wall region is given with little error by the logarithmic mean of the flux at inlet and transition temperatures [2,788 Btu/(h)(ft²) in Example 1]. Strictly, perhaps, the mean flux should be determined at the caloric temperature, as shown by Colburn, who used a graphical method that may not have significantly improved the accuracy of the result [5].

2: Shell-side condensing, plain tube

In this example, propane is cooled from 146°F and condensed at 98°F in a shell-and-tube exchanger. Water at a mean temperature of 82°F flows inside the tubes at 5 ft/s. The tubes are ¾-in. O.D. × 0.65-in. plain wall of 70/30 copper-nickel. Fouling factors of 0.001 (outside) and 0.002 (inside) are specified.

The mean vapor mass-velocity is found to be 122,000 lb/(h)(ft²).

Again, the saturated vapor is considered first. Here, it will be seen that the largest resistance is the one across the condensate film, and that this uses more than half the overall temperature difference (Table II).

The dry-wall calculation at the inlet temperature yields $\Delta T_{ov} - \Delta T_v = 20.57°F$, which is greater than ΔT_{oL} (16°F) and establishes that the surface will be dry.

Following the same procedure, an approximate estimate of 3,325 Btu/(h)(ft²) is obtained for the transition flux. In the present case, there is little error in this determination, because h_c (and consequently U') is almost constant. To show the effect of minor variations in h_c, the calculations have allowed for the small change in coolant film temperature between the two parts of the duty, but usually this would be ignored and h_c assumed constant.

The temperature $T_v = 131.8°F$ is then found for use in the second dry-wall calculation. At this temperature, the calculated $\Delta T_{ov} - \Delta T_v$ is 15.80°F, i.e., below ΔT_{oL}, and so it is in the wet-wall region but close to T_t, which is now estimated by interpolation to be 132.4°F.

The vapor convection heat-transfer coefficient varies little in the dry-wall region and can be interpolated between the two figures already calculated for h_v, giving $h_t = 96.7$ Btu/(h)(ft²)(°F). And from Eq. (5a):

$$\text{Transition flux} = h_t(T_t - T_L) = 96.7 \times 34.4$$
$$= 3{,}327 \text{ Btu/(h)(ft²)}.$$

This result confirms the accuracy of the original approximation.

The logarithmic mean flux over the dry-wall region is 3,784 Btu/(h)(ft²).

In this example, the flux at the transition temperature is more than twice the saturation flux, and the manner in which the flux changes between the two temperatures may be of interest.

Selection of industrial dryers

Here is a discussion of the types of batch and continuous dryers that are available, and a procedure for choosing the most suitable one for a particular process.

C. M. van 't Land, *Akzo Chemie Nederland bv*

☐ Drying is the removal, by heat, of volatile substances (moisture) from a mixture, to yield a solid product [1]. Although this definition includes the drying of such materials as pottery, timber and particulate materials, this article will discuss drying only for the chemical, pharmaceutical and food industries.

Dried material to be sold to customers must meet agreed-upon specifications. To attain these specifications, it may be necessary to assess the conditions of:

- The dryer.
- The equipment preceding the dryer.
- The equipment following the dryer.

The choice of continuous versus batch drying also depends on the nature of the equipment preceding and following the dryer. (Production capacities exceeding 100 kg/h often require use of a continuous dryer.)

Table I contains a list of possible criteria for judging a dried particulate material; Table II outlines the data that may have to be collected before one can start work on selecting a dryer.

Alternatives to full drying

Before drying is attempted, it is worthwhile to consider the possibility of alternatives:

Flaking instead of drying—Materials having a relatively low melting point can be flaked instead of dried. Upon heating of the slurry, the solid phase melts, and a liquid-liquid separation may be made using a disk centrifuge.

Selling wet filter cake—It is possible that the customer may be able to use wet filter cake instead of a dry product. (If the solid dissolves in the liquid only to a very small degree, the cake remains loose; otherwise it may set up and become hard to handle.)

In-product drying—A wet centrifuge- or filter-cake may be dried by admixing it with a material that forms a hydrate, or a higher hydrate, with the water in the wet cake. Heat evolution accompanies the hydration.

Selling product that is not bone-dry—The customer may be willing to accept product that still contains some moisture. The removal of the last quantity of moisture is relatively expensive compared with the removal of the bulk of liquid.

Some drying truisms

If it is possible to remove moisture mechanically, this will always be more economical than removing it by evaporation.

Originally published March 5, 1984

Steam-tube rotary dryers and direct-heat rotary dryers are universally applicable. They can be chosen if there is a limited quantity of experimental data, or insufficient time to go through the selection procedure suggested later in this article. However, the tailor-made solution, using the selection procedures, will often lead to a less expensive solution to the drying problem.

The drying of certain products is almost universally associated with a particular type of dryer that has been found especially suitable. Examples are the use of tunnel dryers for prunes or continuous bin dryers for grain.

Selection schemes

Fig. 1 and 2 are flowcharts for the selection of batch dryers (Fig. 1) and continuous dryers (Fig. 2), both for particulate materials.

Batch dryers

Here are some comments on Fig. 1 (for selection of batch dryers):

Vacuum dryers—If the maximum product temperature is lower than or equal to 30°C, it is worthwhile to look at a vacuum dryer. A good driving force for evaporation can be created while keeping the temperature low. The vacuum tray dryer is the simplest, but the product must usually be sieved to break down any agglomerates (the breakdown may be aided mechanically).

The capacity of the vacuum tray dryer is rather low. It may be economic to consider an agitated vacuum dryer (Fig. 3) in which the contents are moved mechanically. Such dryers are widely used.

If the product is oxidized by air during drying, consider either vacuum drying or inert-gas drying.

If either the product or the removed liquid is toxic, the equipment must be kept closed as much as possible. Again, a vacuum dryer can render good service. (In addition, dust formation is avoided.)

Fluidized-bed dryers—If the average particle size is about 0.1 mm, or larger, fluidized-bed drying (Fig. 4) may be considered. (If smaller particles must be dealt with, the equipment required to handle them may be too large to be feasible.) Inert gas may be used if there is the possibility of explosion of either the vapor or dust in air.

If such a dryer is being considered, it is easy to carry out tests in a small fluid-bed dryer.

Other dryers—As Fig. 1 shows, the remaining possibilities are the tray dryer and the agitated pan dryer.

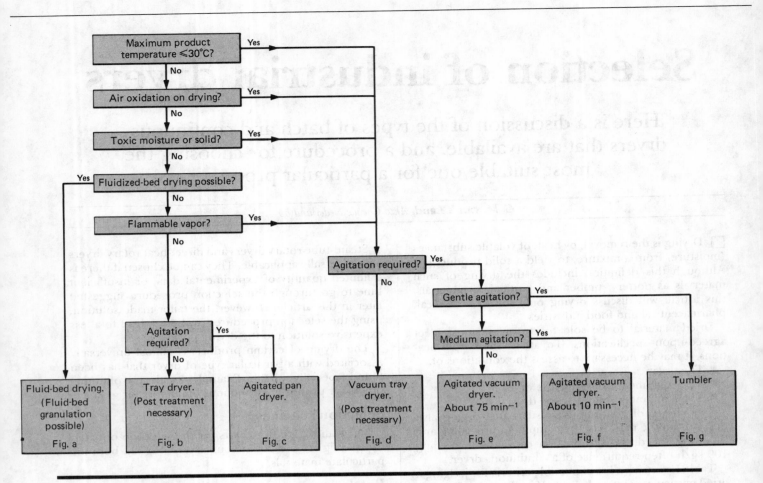

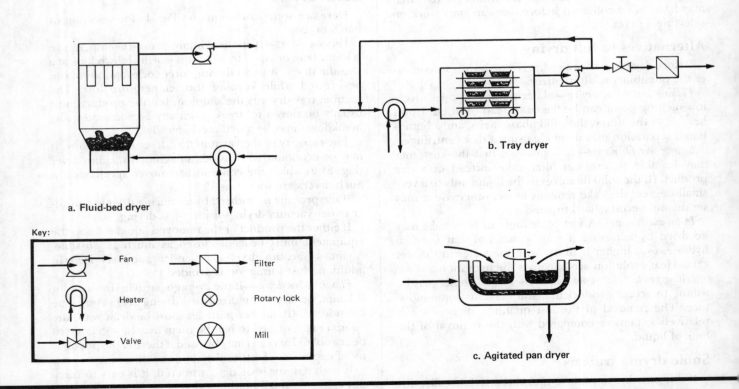

Key:

Fan	Filter
Heater	Rotary lock
Valve	Mill

a. Fluid-bed dryer

b. Tray dryer

c. Agitated pan dryer

Decision tree for the selection of a batch dryer suitable for any particular process need together with sketches of the

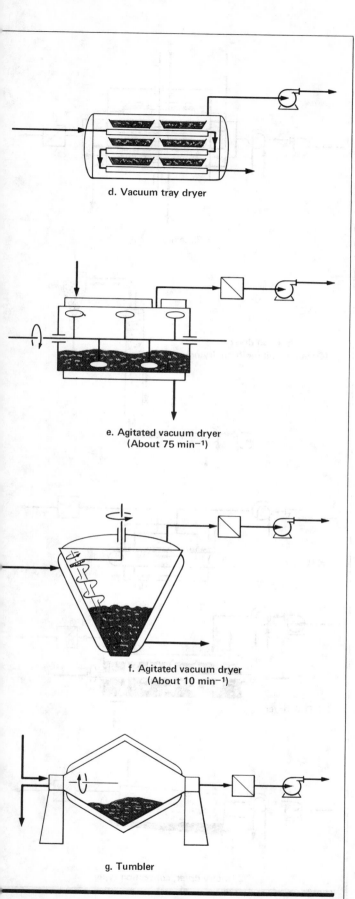

d. Vacuum tray dryer

e. Agitated vacuum dryer
(About 75 min⁻¹)

f. Agitated vacuum dryer
(About 10 min⁻¹)

g. Tumbler

various dryers suggested   **Fig. 1**

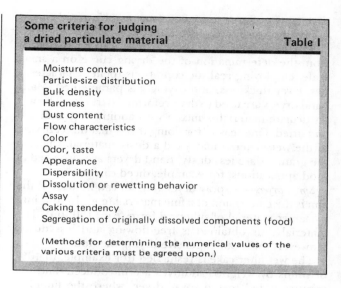

Some criteria for judging a dried particulate material	Table I

Moisture content
Particle-size distribution
Bulk density
Hardness
Dust content
Flow characteristics
Color
Odor, taste
Appearance
Dispersibility
Dissolution or rewetting behavior
Assay
Caking tendency
Segregation of originally dissolved components (food)

(Methods for determining the numerical values of the various criteria must be agreed upon.)

Continuous dryers

Solvent evaporation—In continuous drying, if a solvent must be evaporated and then recovered, it is usually not optimum to choose a convection dryer. Since solvent must be condensed from a large carrier-gas flow, the condenser and other equipment become rather large.

Milling/drying—If it is necessary to decrease particle size, in addition to drying, the two operations may be advantageously combined. The wet particulate solid is transported by warm or hot gas into a mill. Gas and particulate solid leave the mill, fly through a line and are separated. The comminution often greatly helps the drying by exposing internal moisture. This type of drying is encountered in cases where the fineness is of great importance to the application. Examples are cases where a rapid and complete dispersion (or dissolution) or a high activity (m²/g) are being aimed for.

Band (belt) dryers—A band dryer (Fig. 5) is preferable if the particles are rather coarse (i.e., over 5 to 10 mm). The particles are evenly spread onto a slowly moving, e.g., 5 mm/s, perforated belt. The belt moves into a drying cabinet and warm gas passes downward through the layer. This type of dryer is chosen when it is not possible to suspend the particles in the drying gas. The

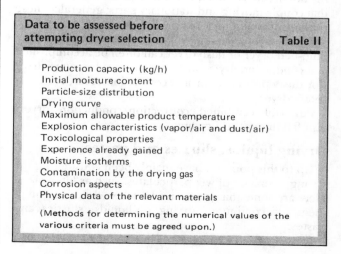

Data to be assessed before attempting dryer selection	Table II

Production capacity (kg/h)
Initial moisture content
Particle-size distribution
Drying curve
Maximum allowable product temperature
Explosion characteristics (vapor/air and dust/air)
Toxicological properties
Experience already gained
Moisture isotherms
Contamination by the drying gas
Corrosion aspects
Physical data of the relevant materials

(Methods for determining the numerical values of the various criteria must be agreed upon.)

dryer must offer a residence time, say 15 min, because bound moisture must diffuse through the pellet.

The performance of such a dryer can be predicted from the determination of the drying curve on a small scale, employing realistic conditions (pellet characteristics, layer thickness, and drying-gas parameters). Many band dryers are used to dry preformed particles. The wet particulate material is mixed with additives, granulated and dried. One reason for doing this is that direct drying of the wet material may yield a dusty material, whereas the granules are less dusty. Band dryers are also used in food applications, for example, diced carrots.

Spray dryers—A spray dryer (Fig. 6) can be used if the aim is the conversion of a fine material (e.g., 15 μm) into a coarser material of spherical form (e.g., 150 μm). The material thus obtained is free-flowing and less dusty. However, this is an expensive drying method.

The wet filter cake is reslurried (for example, to 40% of solids by weight), additives are introduced, and the mixture is fed to the spray dryer, where the liquid is evaporated. To keep the size of the equipment reasonable, a minimum inlet-gas temperature is required (perhaps 200°C) to produce a solids outlet temperature that exceeds 75°C.

Flash dryers—The flash dryer is the workhorse of industry (Fig. 7). However, because drying must take place within 10 s, the removal of bound moisture is difficult. Since the dryer is essentially a vertical line, drying and vertical transport can be combined.

Fluid-bed dryers—Use of a fluid-bed dryer is a possibility if the particle size exceeds 0.1 mm. A round piece of equipment holding a thick product layer is one option. The holdup must be large, as the composition of the dryer contents equals the outlet composition. The thick product layer means that much fan power is needed to push the drying gas through it. Because caking will not easily occur, the construction can be stationary. Such construction can allow high drying-gas temperatures—up to 500–600°C.

A rectangular-shaped dryer will permit plug flow. Fig. 8 shows a stationary type with a thick product layer; a shallow layer may require vibration for transport and to prevent caking. However, a vibrated construction (Fig. 9) cannot withstand high temperatures. A realistic maximum drying-gas inlet temperature is 300°C. Moreover, the hot drying gas must pass through the flexible devices that couple moving and stationary parts; generally, these cannot withstand high temperatures either.

Miscellaneous dryers—Jobs that cannot be handled by the fluid-bed dryer or flash dryer can often be accomplished in a conduction dryer, such as a steam-tube rotary dryer (for dusty products), or in a convection dryer, such as a rotary dryer.

Powerful combined convection/conduction dryers also fall under this heading.

Drying liquids, slurries and pastes

Up to this point we have mainly been considering the drying of masses of wet particulates, such as filter cakes. Here are some things to consider when choosing equipment for continuous drying of liquids, slurries and pastes:

Spray dryers—These may be chosen if the isolation of a

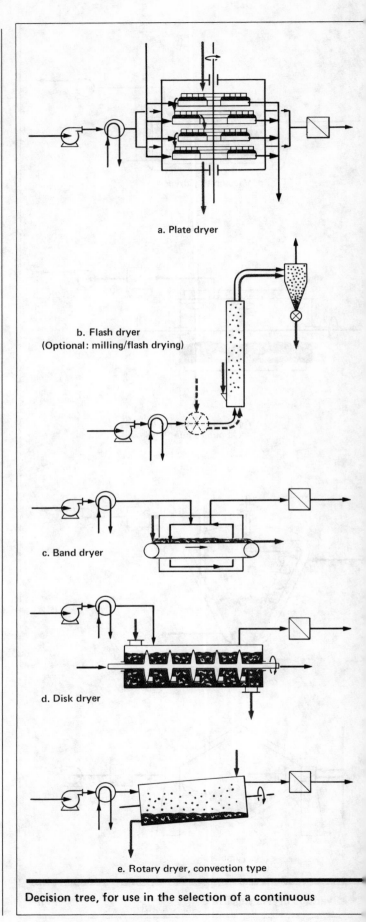

a. Plate dryer

b. Flash dryer
(Optional: milling/flash drying)

c. Band dryer

d. Disk dryer

e. Rotary dryer, convection type

Decision tree, for use in the selection of a continuous

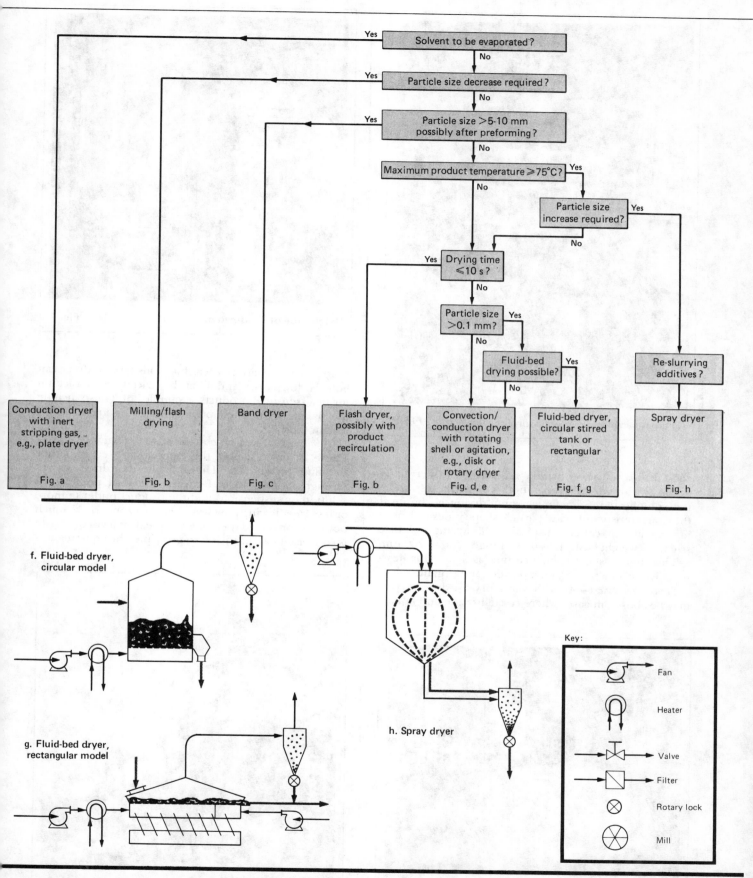

f. Fluid-bed dryer, circular model

g. Fluid-bed dryer, rectangular model

h. Spray dryer

Key:
Fan
Heater
Valve
Filter
Rotary lock
Mill

dryer, leads the user to one of the dryers shown in the sketches

Fig. 2

Jacketed pan dryer employs top-entry agitator   Fig. 9

Bethlehem

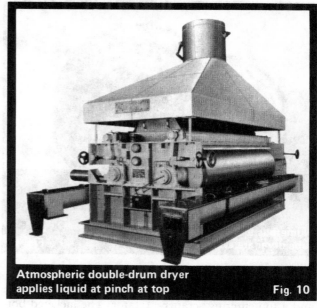

Atmospheric double-drum dryer applies liquid at pinch at top   Fig. 10

Buflovak

is reduced to the desired operating level. The shelves are then heated to the appropriate dehydration temperature. The product is gently dried by heat being conducted from the shelves into the lower portion of the retaining trays, and by heat radiating from the underside of the shelf above. Extremely high vacuum can be readily obtained. The feed is usually a solid, such as a filter cake. The shelf dryer often is used to process extremely dusty and/or expensive material where small quantities must be carefully handled.

Today, the same basic principles are applied to *freeze dryers*. Fig. 7 illustrates a typical system. Here, the design

accommodates a frozen feed, and water is removed by sublimation. The chambers are often modified to provide the ability to stopper ampules or bottles within the chamber, under the operating conditions or selected inert atmospheres. Such dryers frequently find use in the pharmaceutical and food industries.

A more-recent adaptation of the tray dryer, which cuts labor intensiveness and allows continuous operation, is the *plate dryer* (see Fig. 8). In this device, the solids are fed onto the top plate (tray), and gently raked from plate to plate down the unit toward the discharge. Heat is thus conveyed by conduction through the relatively thin bed of material on each plate. The raking provides good mixing, mitigating risks of localized overheating or overdrying of particles, while maintaining close to plug flow. Each plate can be controlled to a different temperature level if desired.

The *pan dryer* (Fig. 9) is a jacketed, flat-bottom, verti-

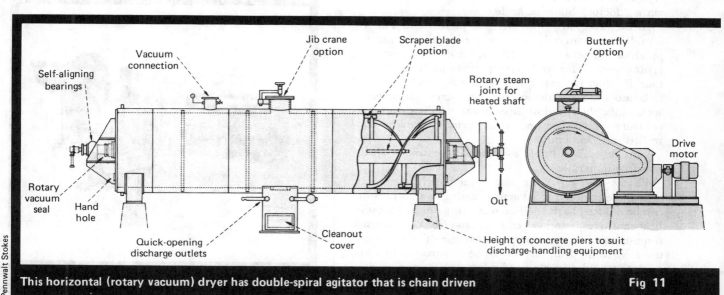

This horizontal (rotary vacuum) dryer has double-spiral agitator that is chain driven   Fig 11

Pennwalt Stokes

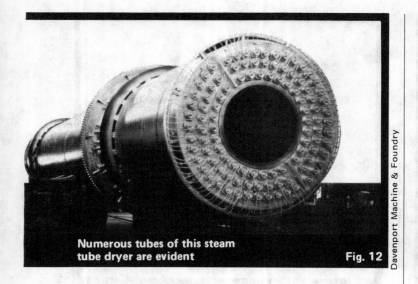

Numerous tubes of this steam tube dryer are evident   **Fig. 12**

Davenport Machine & Foundry

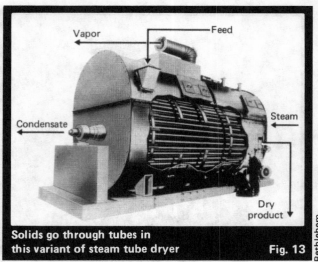

Solids go through tubes in this variant of steam tube dryer   **Fig. 13**

Bethlehem

cal-cylinder-style unit normally having a side discharge and a top-entering scraper/agitator. The jacketed bottom and side walls are heated by steam or circulating heat-transfer oil. The vessel interior may be operated under atmospheric conditions or vacuum (down to 10 mm Hg absolute). A typical agitation system will scrape all of the heat-transfer surfaces, and provide a positive circulation of product outward across the bottom of the dryer toward the side wall but inward from the side wall to the center shaft near the top surface of the bed. Another design incorporates breaker bars to reduce the tendency of product to ball or lump. Feed may be a solid or a slurry. A pan dryer is often used when different products must be handled by the same dryer, since it is particularly easy to clean.

Drum dryers place a thin film of a slurry feed on the surface of an internally heated drum. There are a number of versions, and methods of operation, depending upon application. Variables include: the number of feed-application rolls, the direction of rotation of the rolls, the method of feeding the rolls, film thickness, and type of enclosure. Product is removed from the drum via a "doctor" blade or knife.

In the *atmospheric drum dryer,* as pictured in Fig. 10, liquid feed commonly is introduced at the top, in the pinch or nip between the drums; for slurries, a popular arrangement is for feed to be splashed on from the bottom. Product is scraped off within one revolution, and falls into a removal device, such as a screw conveyor. In such units, the speed of drum rotation, the drum temperature, and other operating variables can be controlled independently.

This dryer is suitable for handling extremely-heat-sensitive materials.

Vacuum drum dryers are also available. In them, the drums are enclosed in a vacuum casing so that pressure can be reduced to the desired operating point. This suits heat-sensitive materials requiring too short a residence time or too low a temperature for use of atmospheric units. Vacuum drum dryers can be constructed to allow operation under sterile conditions, e.g., for the production of pharmaceuticals. (Industrial-sludge drying is an important current application for enclosed- and vac-

uum-type units because they permit complete solvent removal and recovery; dried product serves as a nonpolluting landfill.)

The *horizontal* or *rotary vacuum dryer* (Fig. 11) consists of a cylindrical, jacketed process vessel within which some form of mechanical agitation is provided. Suitable for handling solids or slurries, this unit can be operated either batchwise or continuously.

The agitator can come in several shapes. Its shaft may be hollow, to increase heat-transfer surface. From the shaft, supporting arms project radially. These arms also may be heated. At the ends of the arms, devices such as ribbons, plows or scrapers are attached. These attachments are canted to guide material movement, even if only toward the discharge door. On batch units, this door normally is centrally located.

Fig. 12 illustrates a *steam tube dryer*—basically a cylindrical body in which a number of hollow tubes are arranged symmetrically around the perimeter of the dryer shell. The body is mounted on a set of trunnions in such

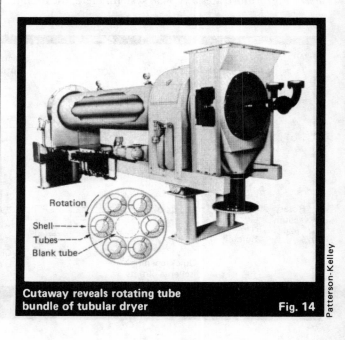

Cutaway reveals rotating tube bundle of tubular dryer   **Fig. 14**

Patterson-Kelley

**Twin Shell dryer is noted
for blending capability**   Fig. 15

Patterson-Kelley

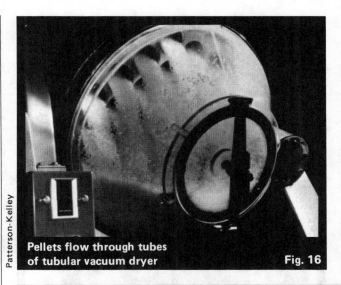

**Pellets flow through tubes
of tubular vacuum dryer**   Fig. 16

Patterson-Kelley

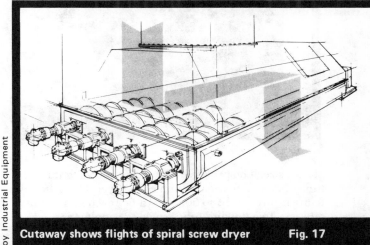

Cutaway shows flights of spiral screw dryer   Fig. 17

Joy Industrial Equipment

**Hollow disc dryer with
centerline-parallel mass flow**   Fig. 18

Bethlehem

a way that the unit is sloped, aiding transport of material through it. The body rotates on the trunnions, providing a tumbling action that continuously exposes fresh material to the heat-transfer surface. Free-flowing feed enters the high end of the body, and tumbles around the steam-heated tubes. Moisture is released continuously to the atmosphere as hot vapor. This type of dryer is often gas-swept to improve the rate of vapor removal and to control the relative humidity of the exhaust gas.

Recently, a different type of steam-tube dryer has appeared on the market—in it, pictured in Fig. 13, material flows through the tubes rather than outside of them. This permits controlled, gentle drying of a wide range of flowing solids. This unit is provided with a limited quantity of sweep air.

The *tubular dryer* (Fig. 14) is almost as old as the conventional steam-tube unit. The shell of this dryer is fixed, and a tube bundle (tube reel) is rotated within it. The bundle is equipped with lifters to elevate the solids fed into the device. The feed thus tumbles down among the tubes, as in the typical steam-tube dryer. The shell is shaped so as to provide a domed vapor space, allowing particle separation without the need for sophisticated dust-removal auxiliaries. The stationary shell eliminates large rotating seals, substituting instead small-diameter shaft seals. Many of these units are used in the starch and brewing industries.

A later development is the *cone* or *twin shell dryer* (Fig. 15). In this batch unit, a jacketed shell rotates about a set of trunnions so as to tumble the solids feed. The vapors generated during the drying cycle are removed through one of the trunnion ends, while the heat-transfer medium enters and exits through the other end. Widely regarded for its blending capabilities, this device is easily cleaned, and finds favor for drying a wide range of heat-sensitive, fragile and coarse materials.

The *tubular vacuum dryer* represents a variation on the cone design. As seen in Fig. 16, this unit essentially consists of a shell-and-tube heat exchanger located between two conical end-sections of the typical cone dryer. The tubes provide a constant heat-transfer-surface/process-volume (s/v) ratio, so drying time is constant regardless

**This hollow disc unit
features axial mass movement**   **Fig. 19**

of unit size. The process cycle takes about one-third the
time of an equal-size vacuum cone dryer. Using hot oil,
temperatures of up to 500°F can be reached. Feed usually is a free-flowing solid, such as a polymer.

Improved surface/volume-ratio designs

Twenty years ago, Horzella [10] pointed out that the
only way to improve the performance of the indirect

dryer is by increasing its s/v ratio. Probably the first
unit developed in response to this was the *spiral screw
dryer* (Fig. 17). The screw flights are hollow, so that
heat-transfer fluid can flow through them. The screw
troughs are fashioned so that one, two or four screw
agitators can be put in a single one, and include a
vaulted area to aid in the disengagement of solid particles from the vapors generated.

A little later, the *hollow disc dryer* appeared in the mar-
ketplace. Two different versions emerged—one (Fig. 18)
in which the mass flow is parallel to the centerline of the
heated disc or perpendicular to the axis of the shaft on
which the discs are mounted; the other (Fig. 19) in
which mass flow is parallel to the axis of the shaft. In
both cases, it is common to employ some sort of clip at
the periphery of the disc to transport the process mass,
and to incorporate a vaulted area in the troughs. Either
design is able to accommodate feed as a slurry or a
solid.

In the first design, the discs are meshed, with a number of shafts being used in a single unit. In the second
design, only one shaft is used per trough, and breaker
bars are installed to increase the mixing of the solids
between the discs. The first variant allows a more complete flooding of the heat-transfer surface.

The *paddle dryer* (Fig. 20) was designed to provide
complete submergence of the heat-transfer surface in
the material being dried. At the same time, the degree
of local mixing around the heat-transfer surface was
increased, resulting in an overall improvement in the
heat-transfer rate. The paddles are hollow and are
heated, as is the shaft. They are arranged on the shaft so
as to provide a discontinuous screw profile, to enhance
movement. One, two or four agitators are incorporated
in each shell. The trough contains a vaulted area for
solids disengagement.

Three other designs round out this compilation:

The *mechanically fluidized dryer* (Fig. 21) consists of a
horizontal, jacketed, cylindrical shell containing a

**Paddle dryer has twin agitators
in omega-shaped trough**   **Fig. 20**

**Mechanically fluidized dryer
employs adjustable paddles**   **Fig. 21**

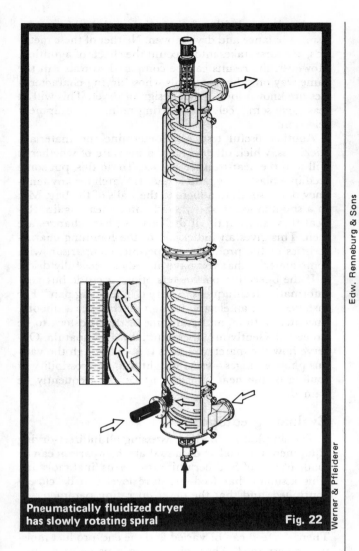

Pneumatically fluidized dryer has slowly rotating spiral   Fig. 22

Werner & Pfleiderer

Edw. Renneburg & Sons

Electrically heated calciner can reach high temperatures   Fig. 23

to dry feedstock prior to its being sent for reduction or calcination.

The importance of pilot testing

Probably the most crucial phase of the indirect-dryer selection process is pilot testing. Indeed, most sales (perhaps eighty-five percent) take place only after such trials. For this reason, manufacturers usually have a laboratory available for demonstrating their equipment with a potential client's feed material. In addition, most can provide rental equipment for actual plant tests. The latter method allows a prospective customer to check the dryer's performance against everyday variation in feed by using a slipstream from the production line.

high-speed agitator. This agitator has narrow, flat, pitched blades, and runs at three to ten times the velocity at which the gravity force on the particles is in balance with centrifugal force. The solid feed, thus, is in a thin layer as it moves across the heated shell. Residence time is relatively short. Often this unit is used with a heated purge-gas stream, thereby combining indirect with direct heat transfer.

Also available is a vertical system that uses conveying air to create a fluidizing condition. In the *pneumatically conveyed dryer* (Fig. 22), material is deposited in a thin film on a vertical, jacketed, cylindrical shell. A heated center shaft, on which air guides are mounted, slowly rotates to ensure good distribution of solids over the heat-transfer surface, preventing dead zones from forming. Feeds usually are fine to powdery solids.

Both of these designs provide a spiral pattern of flow as material advances through them.

An *indirectly heated calciner/dryer* is shown in Fig. 23. It contains a rotating shell housed within a heated chamber. The shell is set between breachings, and rotary seals are used. The chamber is heated either by direct fire or electrically, and temperatures in the thousands of degrees can be reached. So, this unit provides the means to remove water of hydration from many chemicals, and

Checklist of key data for dryer evaluation

Data	Solid	Wetting liquid	Product
Moisture content	R		R
Specific gravity	D	D	D
Bulk density	D		D
Specific heat	D	D	D
Melting point	R		R
Softening point	R		R
Explosive limits	R	R	R
Boiling point		R	
Heat of fusion	A		
Heat of hydration	A		
pH	D	D	D
Sensitivity to heat	R		R
Abrasiveness	R		R
Corrosiveness	R	R	R
Screen analysis	D		R
Temperature of feed	R	R	
Temperature of discharge			R

Key: A = if applicable   D = desired   R = required

Section VI
Other Equipment

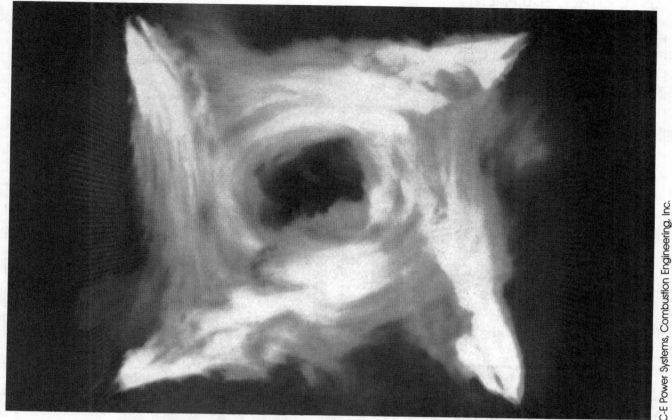

CONTROLLING FIRED HEATERS

Furnaces operated with low excess-air are fuel-efficient
but unstable. Careful instrumentation and control
schemes are necessary to prevent explosion hazards.

Vincent G. Gomes, McGill University

There are two primary objectives in furnace operation—fuel efficiency and safety while maintaining the desired flow, temperature and pressure conditions. The complex interactions between the process variables, and the multiple simultaneous manipulations needed to meet the objectives, make automatic control essential. Split-second decisions required to prevent an explosion hazard in a fuel-efficient furnace (low excess-air operation) are best left to automatic protection systems. Human response-time is inadequate for controlling continuous furnace operations.

Brief review of fundamentals

The factors that determine heater efficiency are:
1. Fluegas exit temperature.
2. Excess-air for combustion.
3. Type of fuel.
4. Heater casing loss.

Improvement in heater efficiency is usually realized by incorporating: a heat-recovery system; improved instrumentation and control; more-efficient burners; improved insulation; efficient soot blowers; reduced air leaks.

Originally published January 7, 1985

Additional heat-recovery equipment has come to be widely used with fired heaters. Design of the heat-recovery system is based on fluegas temperature, dewpoint, and the temperature of the stream that picks up the waste heat. The decision to use such equipment should be based on a technoeconomic feasibility study.

Broadly speaking, heat-recovery systems can include:
1. Process-stream heating in convection section.
2. Steam generation.
3. Air-preheating system for combustion air. Air preheaters are the most widely used heat-recovery system for fired heaters, and are instrumental in boosting the efficiency to about 90%. This article will concentrate on the control and instrumentation of such a system. The important process variables for control of a fired heater with air preheating are:
- Fuel flowrate.
- Air flowrate.
- Operating excess-air.
- Process fluid flowrate.
- Process fluid temperature.
- Furnace draft.
- Flame condition.
- Combustibles.

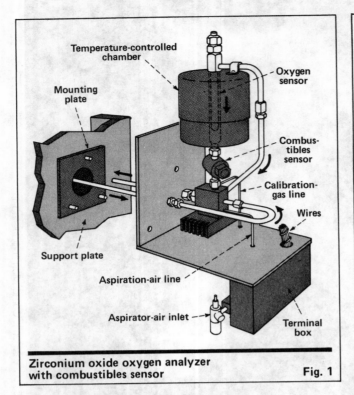

Zirconium oxide oxygen analyzer with combustibles sensor   **Fig. 1**

Pipe size (nominal)	% of differential pressure unrecovered (i.e., pressure loss)*
4	11
5	9
6	21
8	16
10	13
12	11
14	10
16	9
18	8
20	7
24	6
30	5
36	4
42	3
48	3
60	2

Annubar unrecovered pressure loss (typical)   Table I

*By comparison, the total permanent pressure loss for orifice plates is approximately 60% of the differential pressure (rule of thumb)

Choosing a transducer

Good control requires good measuring devices. The focus here will be mainly on primary measuring elements.

Flow measurement

Fuel-oil, and process-fluid, flowrate measurement can be satisfactorily achieved by orifice meters. The fuel-gas flowrate can be corrected by using a densitometer. Air-flow measurement, however, poses some problem, since an orifice produces a high, permanent, pressure loss. The venturimeter yields a low pressure drop, but is comparatively expensive, and may require a duct transition from a rectangular to a circular cross-section. The Annubar element has been found suitable for this job.

The Annubar is an averaging type of flow element. Essentially, an Annubar element has characteristics similar to the pitot tube, but with vastly improved accuracy, ranging within 1% of value based on 95% of test points. It is further reported to have a 0.1%-of-value repeatability, based on an average of various differential-pressure readings. The permanent pressure loss in the Annubar is comparable to that of the venturi tube; hence, it is much less energy-intensive compared with the orifice plate (Table I). Further, the Annubar is relatively insensitive to surface wear or abrasion on edges or sensor parts, ensuring long-term accuracy. However, the overall system accuracy and flow range are limited by the differential-pressure secondary instrumentation (transmitters, meters, etc.). Hence, care must be exercised in the selection of the secondary instruments.

Excess-air estimation

The indicators used to control low-excess-air trim are oxygen and carbon monoxide meters. Controversy exists as to which is preferable, but oxygen analyzers are cheaper and are more widely used. The zirconium-oxide ceramic sensing element has come to be widely preferred. It offers several advantages over the other existing types—such as reduced maintenance requirements, minimum sample-conditioning needs, ability to handle dirty fluegases, and greater resolution at low oxygen content—and is readily adaptable for use as a probe type or extractive type. The extractive type can be used in combination with other suitable monitoring devices such as the combustibles sensor. A portion of the aspirated sample is fed in a closed loop to the sensor (which is housed in a temperature-controlled chamber) and is discharged back to the furnace (Fig. 1).

The sensor output signal is determined with respect to the oxygen content of a reference gas such as air. The electromotive force, E, produced by the cell is given by:

$$E \propto T \log \frac{[O_2]_{\text{Ref. gas}}}{[O_2]_{\text{Sample gas}}}$$

$[O_2]_{\text{Reg. gas}}$ = Concentration of oxygen in reference gas = 0.209 for air; $[O_2]_{\text{Sample gas}}$ = Concentration of oxygen in sample gas; T = Temperature (absolute)

Because its output voltage is temperature-dependent, the cell has to be maintained at a constant temperature. Since the resulting output signal is inversely proportional to the logarithm of the O_2 concentration of the sampled gas, the signal strength is higher at lower concentration. Therefore, greater accuracy, reliability and resolution are obtainable at the lower range of operating excess-air (see Table II).

It is advisable to locate the analyzer installation at the heater breeching, where errors due to air leakage are

Typical oxygen-analyzer specifications   Table II

Accuracy: 1% of excess O_2
Repeatability: 0.2% of measured value
Response time: 5 s (approximate)
Sample temperature: 3,200°F (max.), with ceramic probe
Sample flowrate: 0.1—120 std. ft^3/h
Sample pressure: 2 psig
Aspirator air requirements: 10 to 20 std ft^3/h at
  15 to 100 psi.
Combustibles monitor: Catalytic detector independent
  of O_2 sensor

Typical flame-scanner specifications   Table III

Response range: 190—270 nm (wavelength)
Flame-off delay: 1—3 s (preset)
Power consumption: 15 VA
Temperature range (operating): 0—60°F
Field of view: 3 deg
Purge/cooling air: 1 ft^3/min
"Flame-on" sensitivity: 1 $\mu W/cm^2$
"Fault" sensitivity: 100 $\mu W/cm^2$

expected to be minimum. If the analyzer is mounted at the exit of the convection section or in the fluegas duct, a leak analysis is recommended to determine the required correction to analyzer readings.

Combined O_2 and CO analyzers can be used to trim excess air, if the extra cost is justifiable.

Temperature measurement

Thermocouple temperature measurement is adequate in a heater environment. For better estimation of fluegas temperature, a velocity thermocouple is recommended [1], because of its superior sampling technique.

Flame scanning

Use of forced-draft burners with electrical ignition requires monitoring for flame failure. The ultraviolet flame scanner offers an excellent solution for multiple-burner heaters having combination firing. Typically, the UV cell comprises a pair of highly polished molybdenum (or sometimes tungsten) electrodes positioned at a certain distance from each other inside a helium-filled glass bulb. The gas between the excited electrodes becomes ionized upon being struck by UV photons. The resultant pulse frequency is a direct measure of the radiation intensity received, thus providing a realizable means for discrimination between the main flame and its neighbors.

However, the UV radiation fields are not evenly distributed within a flame envelope; hence, a proper viewing angle across the plane of the flame is required. Besides, it is advisable to eliminate interference from neighboring flames by proper positioning. Usually, each burner is integrally fitted with a UV scanner, factory-set for optimum viewing plane and angle.

The life expectancy of a UV scanner drops drastically with higher operating temperature. Hence, proper housing and use of cooling air, in addition to an air purge for cleaning the optics, are necessary. Table III provides a brief summary of typical specification figures.

In addition to the detecting-tube type, solid-state scanners also are available. However, solid-state devices (diode/transistor) are very temperature-sensitive and require installation at a cool, remote location. Therefore, fiber-optic bundles normally are used for transmitting the light signal to the solid-state detector, which is usually placed not more than 6 ft away. Commercially available fiber-optic bundles exhibit a high attenuation of the UV spectrum, but are considerably better at visible and lower frequencies. Hence, red, far-infrared or far-violet spectra are selected for operation.

Modern flame detectors are designed and located for sensing multiple characteristics of a flame before the presence of the flame is acknowledged. Thus, it is not unusual to find a burner unit fitted with more than one detector head and detector unit logic, including self-checking features, to take care of sensor failure.

Fired-heater control

General description

The main objectives of the control system for a furnace with air preheating are to:
1. Meter fuel according to load demand.
2. Proportion air and fuel for complete combustion.
3. Optimize excess-air for fuel efficiency.
4. Initiate protective measures in the event of a flameout or a fan failure.
5. Maintain optimum draft conditions.
6. Monitor fluegas combustibles and air-preheater cold-end temperature.
7. Monitor process-stream conditions.

There are many possible variations of the control scheme that depend on the particular fired-heater system and the philosophy regarding component failure. A representative scheme will be examined, in the following discussion, over which modifications can be effected to suit a particular system. The controllers most widely used for the analog control system to be described are the parameter-optimized proportional-integral (PI) or the proportional-integral-derivative (PID) type.

Fuel-air control

The firing-rate-demand signal is used for regulating the fuel and air flowrates. This signal is derived from the deviation of the process-fluid outlet condition from that desired (setpoint). The process-fluid outlet condition is usually determined from the fluid temperature. In case of vaporization within a very narrow temperature range, the fluid pressure is used as the feedback. The simultaneous fuel and air control (Fig. 2) employs a cross-limit control system. It ensures that fuel demand does not exceed passes, the LMTD correction factor is usually quite large. This factor is particularly important when a close, or even relatively close, approach is required.

When flow ratios vary widely, a multipass system with an unequal number of passes is used. For such a system, the correction factor can be quite low, though not as low as the corresponding ones for multipass tubular exchangers. Fig. 9 gives approximate values for the correction factor, F, for various pass systems at NTU up to 11 [9].

Fouling is lessened

Fouling is restrained in plate exchangers by highly turbulent flow (which keeps solids in suspension), smooth plate surface, and the absence of low-velocity zones (such as are present on the shell side of tubular exchangers). Corrosion-resistant plate material also reduces fouling tendencies in a plate exchanger, because deposits of corrosion products to which fouling can adhere are absent.

Fouling factors for designing plate exchangers are much less than for shell-and-tube ones, with resistance values of the first being about 10% to 20% of the second. Simplicity of cleaning, whether chemical or mechanical, also allows lower design fouling-factors. Factors recommended for plate-exchanger design are given in Table II, assuming operation at the economic pressure drop of about 0.3 kg/cm² [9].

Curbing corrosion and erosion

Because plates are so thin compared with tubes, corrosion allowances recommended in standard reference books for process equipment are almost meaningless. As a general guide, the maximum permissible corrosion rate for a plate exchanger is 2 mils/yr.

For a particular corrosive environment, a change from a shell-and-tube to a plate exchanger may call for an upgrading of alloy. For example, whereas Type 316 stainless steel is specified for a tubular exchanger cooling sulfuric acid, a plate exchanger may require a 25 Ni, 20 Cr, 4 Mo, 2 Cu alloy, or even Incoloy 825 (40 Ni, 25 Cr, 3 Mo, 2 Cu). The design engineer must depend on the equipment supplier to recommend a suitable material for a specific duty.

Although a plate exchanger may require a more expensive material of construction, the thin gage of plates, with its high heat-transfer coefficient, frequently means that the plate exchanger's cost/unit of heat transfer is lower.

Plate geometry, in addition to promoting turbulent flow, also intensifies erosion. Therefore, materials such as cupro-nickel alloys used in tubular exchangers are not suitable for plate exchangers.

For these exchangers, materials, such as Monel or titanium, that combine excellent corrosion resistance to the chloride ion with immunity to erosion-corrosion should be specified [10].

Heat transfer and pressure-drop correlations

The film coefficients of heat transfer for plate exchangers are usually correlated by an equation such as:

$$Nu = CRe^n Pr^m (\mu_{av}/\mu_w)^x \qquad (3)$$

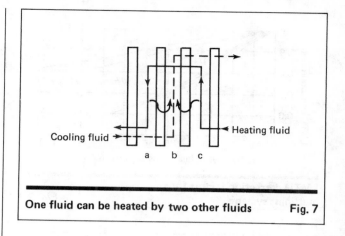

Cooling fluid   Heating fluid

a b c

One fluid can be heated by two other fluids   **Fig. 7**

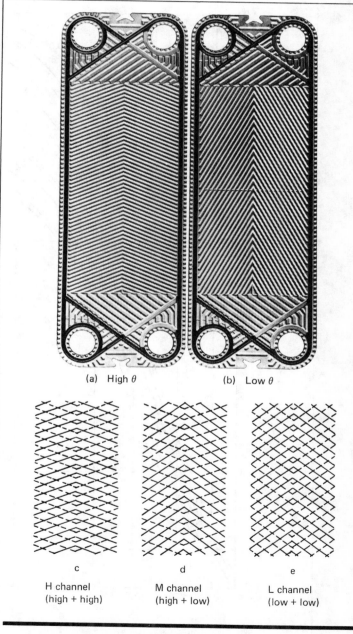

(a) High θ   (b) Low θ

c   d   e

H channel   M channel   L channel
(high + high)   (high + low)   (low + low)

High and low θ plates can be combined   **Fig. 8**

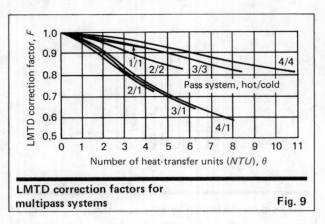

LMTD correction factors for multipass systems **Fig. 9**

The constants and exponents are determined empirically and are valid only for a particular plate design. Typical reported values for turbulent flow are [9]: $C = 0.15$ to 0.40; $n = 0.65$ to 0.85; $m = 0.30$ to 0.45 (usually 0.333); and $x = 0.05$ to 0.20.

A widely adopted correlation for estimating film coefficients for turbulent flow in plate exchangers is [11]:

$$h = 0.2536(k/D_e)(Re_{av})^{0.65}(Pr_{av})^{0.4} \qquad (4)$$

The equivalent diameter, D_e, is defined as four times the cross-sectional area of the channel, divided by the wetted perimeter of the channel, or:

$$D_e = (4Wb)/(2W + 2b) \qquad (5)$$

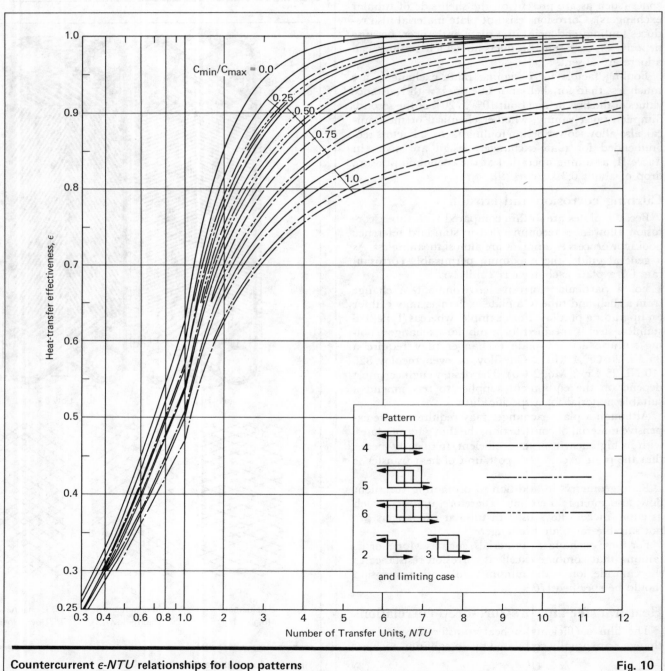

Countercurrent ϵ-NTU relationships for loop patterns **Fig. 10**

In Eq. (5), D_e equals approximately $2b$, because b is negligible in comparison with W.

For laminar flow (Re < 400), Jackson, et al., proposed the equation [12]:

$$h = 0.742 C_p G (Re_{av})^{-0.62} \times$$
$$(Pr_{av})^{-0.667} (\mu_{av}/\mu_w)^{0.14} \quad (6)$$

Flow is normally laminar in plate exchangers handling highly viscous and polymeric materials.

Pressure drop in a plate exchanger can be estimated by the equations recommended by Cooper [13]:

$$\Delta P = (2 f G^2 L)/(g D_e \rho) \quad (7)$$

In Eq. (7), $f = 2.5/Re^{0.3}$.

These equations represent highly simplified situations. Any accurate estimation of pressure drop should take into consideration the plate geometry, as well as the pressure losses in the ports.

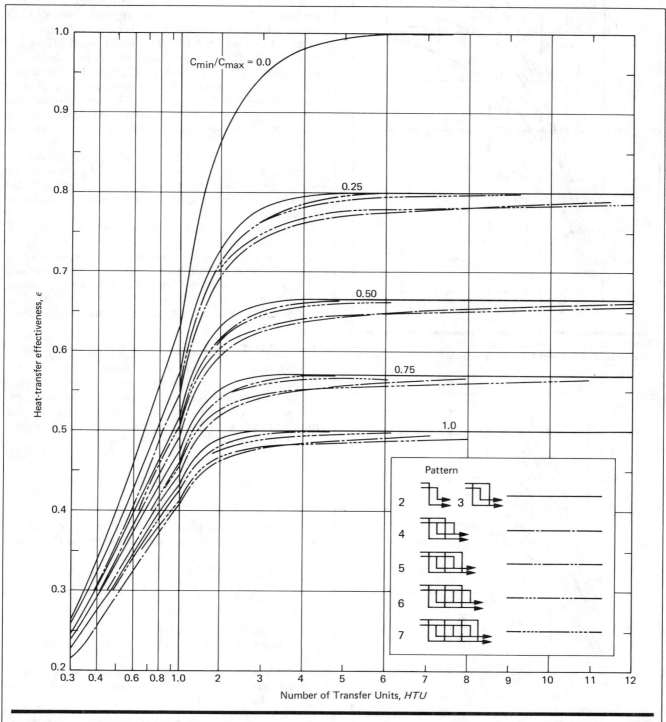

Cocurrent ϵ-NTU relationships for loop patterns   **Fig. 11**

Average velocities in plate exchangers are lower than in tubular exchangers. Velocities typically range from 0.5 to 0.8 m/s in plate heat exchangers, and 1 m/s in tubular ones. However, because of the highly turbulent flow in plate exchangers, heat-transfer coefficients are much higher than in tubular exchangers [e.g., for water, 2,500–3,500 kcal/(h)(m²)(°C) compared with 1,000–

1,500 kcal/(h)(m²)(°C)]. The required heat transfer can be achieved with fewer passes in the plate than in the tubular exchanger.

Design procedures

The complexities of plate designs and flow configurations limit the application of available information (which is scanty) on plate exchangers. Manufacturers have their own design procedures for their exchangers, which involve elaborate computer programs.

Basically, there are two approaches in plate-exchanger design [9,11,14]. One approach uses LMTD correction factors; the other, heat-transfer effectiveness, ϵ, as a function of NTU. The main assumptions involved in both design methods are: (1) heat losses are negligible; (2) there are no air pockets in the exchanger; (3) the average overall heat-transfer coefficient is constant throughout the exchanger; (4) channel temperatures vary only in the flow direction; and (5) the streams split equally between channels in the case of parallel flow.

If N is the number of thermal plates, the number of channels formed will be $(N + 1)$. (Only the thermal plates transfer heat; the two end plates do not, one reason why plate units require less insulation than tubular units, or none at all.)

The design procedures can be best illustrated by a typical problem.

Given: (1) hot-fluid inlet and outlet temperatures and flowrates, (2) cold-fluid inlet temperature and flowrate, (3) physical properties of the fluids, and (4) physical characteristics of the plates.

Required: The area for both series- and parallel-flow exchangers.

The LMTD approach

This modified form of the method reported by Buonopane et al. [11] applies for both series and parallel flow patterns, except as noted. Considerations involved in the selection of flow patterns, including the number of passes for parallel flows, have been discussed.

1. Calculate the heat load via Eq. (8):

$$q = (w C_p \Delta t)_h \tag{8}$$

2. Calculate cold-fluid exit temperature:

$$t_{co} = t_{ci} + (q/(w C_p)_c) \tag{9}$$

3. Determine the physical properties of the fluids at the arithmetic average of their exchanger inlet and outlet temperatures.

4. Calculate LMTD:

$$\text{LMTD} = \frac{(t_{hi} - t_{co}) - (t_{ho} - t_{ci})}{\ln[(t_{hi} - t_{co})/(t_{ho} - t_{ci})]} \tag{10}$$

5. Calculate NTU via Eq. (2).

6. Determine the LMTD correction factor from Fig. 9.

7. Calculate the Reynolds number for each stream. For (a) series flow (each fluid passes as one single stream through the channels):

$$Re = (D_e G)/\mu \tag{11a}$$

For (b) parallel flow, assume the number of thermal

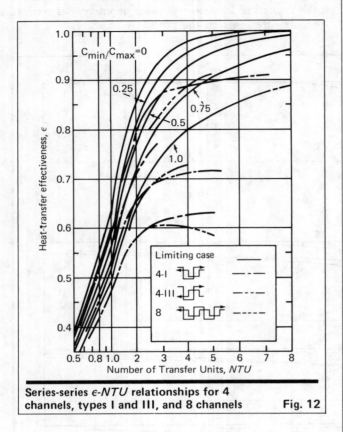

Series-series ϵ-NTU relationships for 4 channels, types I and III, and 8 channels   **Fig. 12**

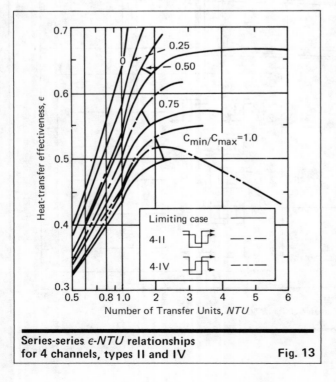

Series-series ϵ-NTU relationships for 4 channels, types II and IV   **Fig. 13**

plates and determine the number of substreams, n_c and n_h, into which each fluid is divided:

$$Re = [D_e(G/n)]/\mu \qquad (11b)$$

8. Calculate heat-transfer coefficients from either Eq. (4) or (6), depending upon whether Re is, respectively, greater or less than 400.

9. Calculate the overall heat-transfer coefficient:

$$U_{av} = 1/[(1/h_h) + (x/k)_p + (1/h_c) + d_{f_h} + d_{f_c}] \qquad (12)$$

10. Calculate total heat-transfer area:

$$A_t = q/(U_{av}\text{LMTD } F) \qquad (13)$$

11. Calculate the number of thermal plates:

$$N = A_t/A_p \qquad (14)$$

12. For parallel flow, from the number of thermal plates calculated in Step 11, determine n for the hot and cold streams. If N is an odd number, n_h and n_c will be equal. If N is an even number, n_h and n_c will be unequal, and one of the fluids will have one more substream than the other (e.g., if $N = 4$ then $n_c = 3$ and $n_h = 2$, or $n_c = 2$ and $n_h = 3$).

13. Compare values of n_c and n_h determined in Step 12 with the corresponding values assumed in Step 7b. If the calculated values do not agree with the assumed values, repeat Steps 7b through 13, replacing assumed values with the values calculated in Step 12, until the values agree.

Steps 1 to 11 are common for both series and parallel flows. Steps 12 and 13 apply only to parallel flow.

Effectiveness-NTU approach

Jackson and Troupe have reported a design procedure that does not involve LMTD correction factors [14]. The concepts of heat-transfer effectiveness, NTU and fluid heat-capacity ratio are instead made use of in the development of the method that can be applied to plate exchangers having different plate and flow configurations.

Although the procedure is suitable for computer programming, the results can also be presented in four diagrams (Fig. 10, 11, 12 and 13) that give ε-NTU relationships as a function of flow patterns and fluid heat-capacity ratios. The procedure can be illustrated in the following steps:

1. Calculate the heat load via Eq. (8).
2. Calculate cold-fluid exit temperature via Eq. (9).
3. Determine the physical properties of the fluids at the arithmetic average of their inlet and outlet temperatures.
4. Calculate heat-transfer effectiveness:

$$\varepsilon = \frac{(wC_p)_h(t_{hi} - t_{ho})}{(wC_p)_{min}(t_{hi} - t_{ci})}$$
$$= \frac{(wC_p)_c(t_{co} - t_{ci})}{(wC_p)_{min}(t_{hi} - t_{ci})} \qquad (15)$$

5. Calculate heat-capacity ratio, $(wC_p)_{min}/(wC_p)_{max}$.
6. Assume an exchanger containing an infinite number of channels and find the required NTU, using the appropriate ε-NTU relationship (Fig. 10, 11, 12 and 13).
7. Calculate the Reynolds number for each stream.

For series flow, use Eq. (11a). For parallel flow, assume the number of thermal plates and find the number of substreams, n_c and n_h, into which each fluid is divided, using Eq. (11b).

8. Calculate heat-transfer coefficients with Eq. (4) or (6), depending upon whether Re is, respectively, greater or less than 400.

9. Calculate the overall heat-transfer coefficient, using Eq. (12).

10. Calculate the approximate number of thermal plates:

$$N = NTU(wC_p)_{min}/(U_{av}A_p) \qquad (16)$$

11. Assume an exchanger of $(N + 1)$ channels and

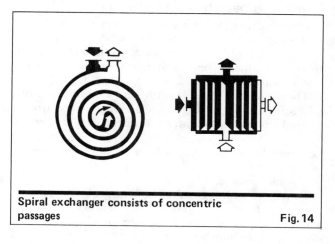

Spiral exchanger consists of concentric passages   **Fig. 14**

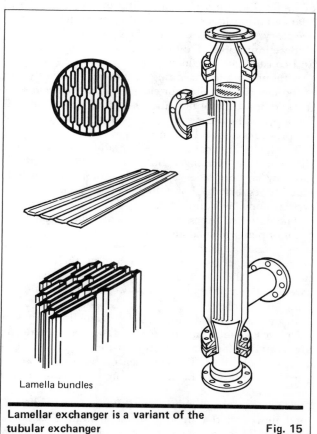

Lamella bundles

Lamellar exchanger is a variant of the tubular exchanger   **Fig. 15**

The program is initially devised for operating in metric units (see Nomenclature). If you wish to work in English units, then press f e; that converts the Regnault formula into these last units. This must be done at the beginning (i.e., before Key A is pressed).

Assumptions

The assumptions made for the mathematical analysis have the following limits:

The feed is at its boiling point—This is not really a limiting condition. It is only a general basis on which to compare results. If the feed is *not* at its boiling point (bp), the extra steam consumption to heat it to the boiling point can be estimated easily by hand calculations. Generally, in industrial situations, the condensed steam is used to preheat the feed in another heat exchanger, so the feed usually reaches its bp.

All the heating surfaces are equal—This is quite normal, especially in the design of industrial evaporators, due to economic considerations.

Sensible heats are negligible when compared with latent heats—This is true in the majority of the cases when the boiling-point rise (bpr) is negligible. The maximum possible error is about 20%—when the solutions are very concentrated and the bpr cannot be overlooked (see next point).

Boiling-point rise is negligible—This is the most limiting condition. It is true when the solution's molal concentration is not too high (according to Raoult's law), or when we deal with solutions of organic compounds of high molecular weights. On the other hand, when we deal with electrolytic compounds, and when the range of concentration is also very wide, the error of the estimated area can be as high as 25 to 35%.

This can be easily computed by adding the bpr of each stage (ΔT_e) and comparing this value with the thermic potential, ΔT, of the evaporator $(\Delta T = t_0 - t_N)$. If $\Sigma(\Delta T_e)_i$ is 30 or 40% of ΔT, then we can expect a high level of error (35%). This error can be 40% when the number of stages is very high (7 or more).

Nevertheless, this is not a serious problem because this program is only designed to find the approximate value of the evaporation area, the most important parameter in design considerations. It is also possible to correct the area as follows:

$$A_{\text{corrected}} = A_{\text{computed}} \frac{\Delta T}{\Delta T \Sigma(\Delta T_e)_i}$$

Example

Find the value of the variables for a three-effect evaporator system.

Data:

$L_0 = 1,000$ kg/h; $T_0 = 100°C$; $x_0 = 0.1$;
$T_N = 60°C$; $x_N = 0.2$
$U_1 = 200$ kcal/h m^2 °C
$U_2 = 400$
$U_3 = 800$

Results:

$L_N = 500$ kg/h;
$T_1 = 77.1$ °C; $T_2 = 65.7$ °C; $T_3 = 60.0$ °C;
$V_0 = 173.6$ kg/h;

$A = 20.4$ m^2
$Q = 93,243$ kcal/h
$V_1 = 168.6$ kg/h; $V_2 = 166.3$ kg/h; $V_3 = 165.1$ kg/h;
$L_1 = 831.3$ kg/h; $L_2 = 665.1$ kg/h; $L_3 = 500.0$ kg/h;
$r = 2.88$
$x_1 = 0.12$; $x_2 = 0.15$; $x_3 = 0.20$

For TI-58/59 users

The TI version of the program appears in Table II. User instructions are found in Table III, and the example is run in Table IV.

Program listing for TI version   Table II

Step	Code	Key	Step	Code	Key	Step	Code	Key
000	76	LBL	023	14	14	046	43	RCL
001	10	E'	024	91	R/S	047	00	00
002	86	STF	025	42	STO	048	42	STO
003	00	00	026	15	15	049	58	58
004	01	1	027	02	2	050	43	RCL
005	01	1	028	42	STO	051	19	19
006	01	1	029	00	00	052	55	÷
007	04	4	030	91	R/S	053	43	RCL
008	42	STO	031	76	LBL	054	15	15
009	59	59	032	12	B	055	65	×
010	91	R/S	033	35	1/X	056	43	RCL
011	76	LBL	034	72	ST*	057	13	13
012	11	A	035	00	00	058	95	=
013	42	STO	036	32	X:T	059	42	STO
014	19	19	037	01	1	060	16	16
015	91	R/S	038	44	SUM	061	98	ADV
016	42	STO	039	00	00	062	99	PRT
017	01	01	040	32	X:T	063	98	ADV
018	91	R/S	041	91	R/S	064	43	RCL
019	42	STO	042	76	LBL	065	58	58
020	13	13	043	13	C	066	32	X:T
021	91	R/S	044	58	FIX	067	02	2
022	42	STO	045	02	02	068	42	STO

Step	Code	Key	Step	Code	Key	Step	Code	Key	Step	Code	Key	Step	Code	Key
069	00	00	133	00	00	197	01	01	261	98	ADV	325	99	PRT
070	76	LBL	134	32	X:T	198	95	=	262	42	STO	326	01	1
071	22	INV	135	43	RCL	199	65	×	263	21	21	327	44	SUM
072	73	RC*	136	58	58	200	43	RCL	264	02	2	328	00	00
073	00	00	137	75	-	201	12	12	265	42	STO	329	43	RCL
074	44	SUM	138	01	1	202	95	=	266	00	00	330	00	00
075	17	17	139	95	=	203	35	1/X	267	43	RCL	331	67	EQ
076	01	1	140	77	GE	204	65	×	268	58	58	332	45	Y×
077	44	SUM	141	23	LNX	205	53	(	269	32	X:T	333	61	GTO
078	00	00	142	98	ADV	206	43	RCL	270	76	LBL	334	44	SUM
079	43	RCL	143	87	IFF	207	19	19	271	42	STO	335	76	LBL
080	00	00	144	00	00	208	75	-	272	43	RCL	336	45	Y×
081	67	EQ	145	34	√X	209	43	RCL	273	21	21	337	98	ADV
082	24	CE	146	06	6	210	16	16	274	55	÷	338	53	(
083	61	GTO	147	00	0	211	54	)	275	53	(	339	43	RCL
084	22	INV	148	06	6	212	95	=	276	43	RCL	340	19	19
085	76	LBL	149	93	.	213	99	PRT	277	59	59	341	75	-
086	24	CE	150	05	5	214	98	ADV	278	75	-	342	43	RCL
087	53	(	151	42	STO	215	42	STO	279	93	.	343	16	16
088	43	RCL	152	59	59	216	20	20	280	06	6	344	54	)
089	14	14	153	76	LBL	217	65	×	281	09	9	345	55	÷
090	75	-	154	34	√X	218	43	RCL	282	05	5	346	43	RCL
091	43	RCL	155	43	RCL	219	17	17	283	65	×	347	20	20
092	01	01	156	58	58	220	65	×	284	73	RC*	348	95	=
093	54	)	157	32	X:T	221	53	(	285	00	00	349	99	PRT
094	55	÷	158	02	2	222	43	RCL	286	54	)	350	98	ADV
095	43	RCL	159	42	STO	223	59	59	287	95	=	351	02	2
096	17	17	160	00	00	224	75	-	288	99	PRT	352	42	STO
097	95	=	161	76	LBL	225	93	.	289	72	ST*	353	00	00
098	42	STO	162	33	X²	226	06	6	290	00	00	354	76	LBL
099	18	18	163	43	RCL	227	09	9	291	01	1	355	52	EE
100	02	2	164	59	59	228	05	5	292	44	SUM	356	43	RCL
101	42	STO	165	75	-	229	65	×	293	00	00	357	19	19
102	00	00	166	93	.	230	43	RCL	294	43	RCL	358	65	×
103	76	LBL	167	06	6	231	01	01	295	00	00	359	43	RCL
104	23	LNX	168	09	9	232	54	)	296	67	EQ	360	13	13
105	73	RC*	169	05	5	233	55	÷	297	43	RCL	361	55	÷
106	00	00	170	65	×	234	53	(	298	61	GTO	362	73	RC*
107	65	×	171	73	RC*	235	43	RCL	299	42	STO	363	00	00
108	43	RCL	172	00	00	236	01	01	300	76	LBL	364	95	=
109	18	18	173	95	=	237	75	-	301	43	RCL	365	72	ST*
110	95	=	174	35	1/X	238	43	RCL	302	98	ADV	366	00	00
111	32	X:T	175	44	SUM	239	14	14	303	43	RCL	367	99	PRT
112	01	1	176	12	12	240	54	)	304	19	19	368	01	1
113	22	INV	177	01	1	241	95	=	305	42	STO	369	44	SUM
114	44	SUM	178	44	SUM	242	99	PRT	306	22	22	370	00	00
115	00	00	179	00	00	243	98	ADV	307	02	2	371	43	RCL
116	73	RC*	180	43	RCL	244	43	RCL	308	42	STO	372	00	00
117	00	00	181	00	00	245	20	20	309	00	00	373	67	EQ
118	85	+	182	67	EQ	246	65	×	310	43	RCL	374	53	(
119	32	X:T	183	35	1/X	247	53	(	311	58	58	375	61	GTO
120	95	=	184	61	GTO	248	43	RCL	312	32	X:T	376	52	EE
121	99	PRT	185	33	X²	249	59	59	313	76	LBL	377	76	LBL
122	32	X:T	186	76	LBL	250	75	-	314	44	SUM	378	53	(
123	01	1	187	35	1/X	251	93	.	315	43	RCL	379	58	FIX
124	44	SUM	188	43	RCL	252	06	6	316	22	22	380	09	09
125	00	00	189	59	59	253	09	9	317	75	-	381	22	INV
126	32	X:T	190	75	-	254	05	5	318	73	RC*	382	86	STF
127	72	ST*	191	93	.	255	65	×	319	00	00	383	00	00
128	00	00	192	06	6	256	43	RCL	320	95	=	384	98	ADV
129	01	1	193	09	9	257	01	01	321	72	ST*	385	91	R/S
130	44	SUM	194	05	5	258	54	)	322	00	00			
131	00	00	195	65	×	259	95	=	323	42	STO			
132	43	RCL	196	43	RCL	260	99	PRT	324	22	22			

User instructions for TI version

Table III

Step		Key	Output
1.	Clear registers	Press **CMs**	
2.	Enter data:		
	Feed flowrate, L_0	Press **A**	L_0
	Steam temperature, T_0	Press **R/S**	T_0
	Feed-liquor concentration, x_0	Press **R/S**	x_0
	Product temperature, T_N	Press **R/S**	T_N
	Product concentration, x_N	Press **R/S**	2
3.	Enter heat-transfer coefficients for each unit:		
	U_1	Press **B**	$1/U_1$
	U_2	Press **B**	$1/U_2$
Output will be:			
	Product flowrate		L_N
	Liquor temperature for each effect		T_i ($i = 1$ to n)
	Steam flowrate		V_0
	Heating surface		A
	Heat load		Q
	Steam flowrate for each effect		V_i ($i = 1$ to n)
	Liquor flowrate to each effect		L_i ($i = 1$ to n)
	Ratio of steam produced/consumed		r
	Liquor concentration for each effect		x_i ($i = 1$ to n)

Example for TI version

Table IV

Enter	Display	Output
Data:		
1000 **A**	1000	
100 **R/S**	100	
0.1 **R/S**	0.1	
60 **R/S**	60	
0.2 **R/S**	2 (Note: 2 is displayed, not 0.2)	
200 **B**	0.005	
400 **B**	0.0025	
800 **B**	0.00125	
Run program:		
C	L_N	500.00
	T_1	77.14
	T_2	65.71
	T_3	60.00
	V_0	173.64
	A	20.40
	Q	93243.46
	V_1	168.65
	V_2	166.26
	V_3	165.09
	L_1	831.35
	L_2	665.09
	L_3	500.00
	r	2.88
	x_1	0.12
	x_2	0.15
	x_3	0.20

The authors

Santiago Esplugas Vidal is a professor of chemical engineering at the University of Barcelona. He holds B.S. and Ph.D. degrees in chemistry from the University of Barcelona. His research areas are simulation of chemical processes and photoreactor engineering.

Juan Mata Alvarez is a professor of chemical engineering at the University of Barcelona, Spain. He has B.S. and Ph.D. degrees from the University of Barcelona. His research focuses on simulation of chemical processes and biologic treatment of wastewater.

Heat transfer in agitated vessels

Easy-to-use procedures set forth how to calculate heat transfer in agitated vessels for continuous and batch operations. They show how to establish heat-transfer coefficients, specify heat-transfer areas for jackets and coils, and determine heating- and cooling-cycle periods.

Frederick Bondy and *Shepherd Lippa*, *The Heyward-Robinson Co.*

☐ Heat transfer in agitated vessels depends on the type of agitator and jacketing or internal coils. An agitator is selected on the basis of the properties of the material and the processing required. Some typical agitators are shown in Fig. 1. Some common jacketing and coil arrangements are depicted in Fig. 2.

In general, the heat transfer occurs as part of a processing operation, such as suspending or dissolving solids, or dispersing a gas, in a liquid; emulsifying immiscible liquids; or regulating chemical reactions. The type, size, location and speed of an agitator will usually be set by such a mixing requirement [1,2,3,4]. In most cases, the agitator and the power it requires are determined before heat-transfer aspects are considered.

When processing is controlled by heat transfer, such variables as log mean temperature difference and transfer surface area will usually predominate over the agitator variables. Mixing can only affect the inside film resistance, which is but one of a number of resistances that determine the overall heat-transfer coefficient.

General relationships

Heat transfer in an agitated vessel having an external jacket follows the relationship $Q = UA \Delta T$. The overall heat-transfer coefficient, U, is determined from a series of five resistances to the transfer of heat:

$$1/U = 1/h_i + ff_i + x/k + ff_j + 1/h_j \qquad (1)$$

Besides applying only to jacketed vessels, Eq. (1) also is only valid when the vessel's diameter is very large in comparison to its wall thickness—i.e., the inner and outer heat-transfer surfaces are very nearly equal—as will be the case with almost all jacketed vessels. When, however, heat is transferred via internal coils or tubular baffles, the difference between the inner and outer heat-transfer surfaces is significant.

The term h_i represents the heat-transfer coefficient on the process side—i.e., the *inside* wall of a vessel having an external jacket, but the *outside* wall of a coil inside a vessel. With internal coils, the coefficient U must be referred to the inner or outer coil surface. The outer surface coefficient, U_o, is also established from a series of five resistances, but is calculated via Eq. (2), which involves coil diameter:

$$\frac{1}{U_o} = \frac{1}{h_i} + ff_i + \left(\frac{x}{k}\right)\left(\frac{d_{co}}{d_{cm}}\right) + \left(\frac{1}{h_{ci}}\right)\left(\frac{d_{co}}{d_{ci}}\right) + ff_{ci} \quad (2)$$

Note that in Eq. (2), h_i represents the film coefficient on the outside wall of the coils.

Continuous vs. batch operation

When the vessel and its jacket (or coil) are operated continuously under isothermal conditions, the general equation $Q = UA \Delta T$ is applied directly. When the vessel is operated continuously with its contents at constant temperature but with different inlet and outlet jacket temperatures, the general equation becomes $Q = UA \Delta T_{lm}$. In both cases, U is constant, but in the latter the temperature difference is the log mean temperature difference between the vessel temperature and the inlet and outlet jacket temperatures.

In the case of batch operation, with the vessel's contents at temperature t_1 initially, and at t_2 after θ hours, Eq. (3) represents the relationship for heating and Eq. (4) for cooling:

$$\ln\left(\frac{T - t_1}{T - t_2}\right) = \left(\frac{UA}{m\,c_p}\right)\theta \qquad (3)$$

$$\ln\left(\frac{t_1 - T}{t_2 - T}\right) = \left(\frac{UA}{m\,c_p}\right)\theta \qquad (4)$$

Here, T is the constant jacket (or coil) temperature, and m is the weight and c_p the specific heat of the vessel's contents.

When the jacket temperature is not constant, Eq. (3) and (4) can still be used if the difference between the jacket inlet and outlet temperatures is small compared with the ΔT_{lm} between the average temperature of the jacket and the temperature of the vessel's contents. However, to use the average jacket temperature for T, the change in the jacket's inlet and outlet temperatures should not be greater than 10% of the ΔT_{lm}. When the

Originally published April 4, 1983

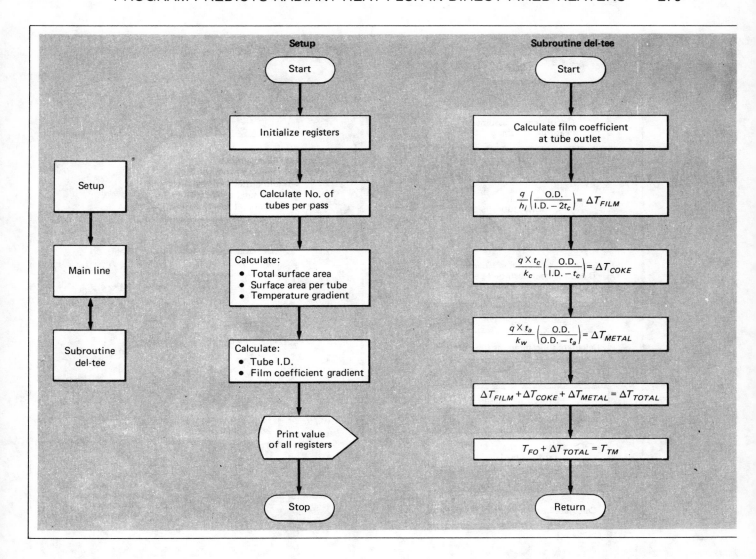

7. Repeat this two-way iterative process until the solution converges to a stable value.

A program is presented for use on the TI-59. This program is adaptable to the HP-97, or to any other programmable calculator.

The program is divided into three sections: setup, mainline and subroutine "del-tee." The logic diagram for the program appears in the figure. The program is shown in Table I, and program storage-allocation appears in Table II.

User's instructions

1. Initialize the following registers: 03, 05, 06, 07, 09, 10, 11, 12, 13, 14, 15, 16, 19 and 23.

2. Enter a first guess for the heat flux at the coil outlet and press **A**. The calculator will go through setup and print out the values of all its registers.

3. Press **E**. The calculator will give a printout of absorption, fluid temperature, tube metal temperature and heat flux at the outlet of each tube.

4. The calculator will also print the value of the calculated total heat absorbed in the coil. If this value is not close enough to the actual heat absorption, guess another value for the heat flux and press **A**, then press **E**.

Notes

The author has found out that a good first guess that forces the program to converge readily is to use a value somewhat less than that of the average heat flux for the whole coil.

A Newton-Raphson or interval-halving [2] subroutine could have been used to force the program to the next guess. Since this requires a substantial increase in both program size and execution time, and since by the above method of guessing we always know the correctness of the second assumption made, the addition of a convergence subroutine cannot be justified.

To obtain the maximum tube-metal temperatures (defined as the temperature of the front 60 deg of the tube), multiply the above TMTs by 1.8. This number, given by API [1], is for tubes arranged in single rows against a wall, and on center-to-center spacing equal to twice the nominal tube diameter.

Example

Data for an example are given in Table II. The heater has 64 tubes arranged in an 8-pass flow. The coil tubes are Sch. 40A pipe, with a thickness of 0.280 in. The thermal conductivity of coke—3.0 Btu/(h)(ft^2)

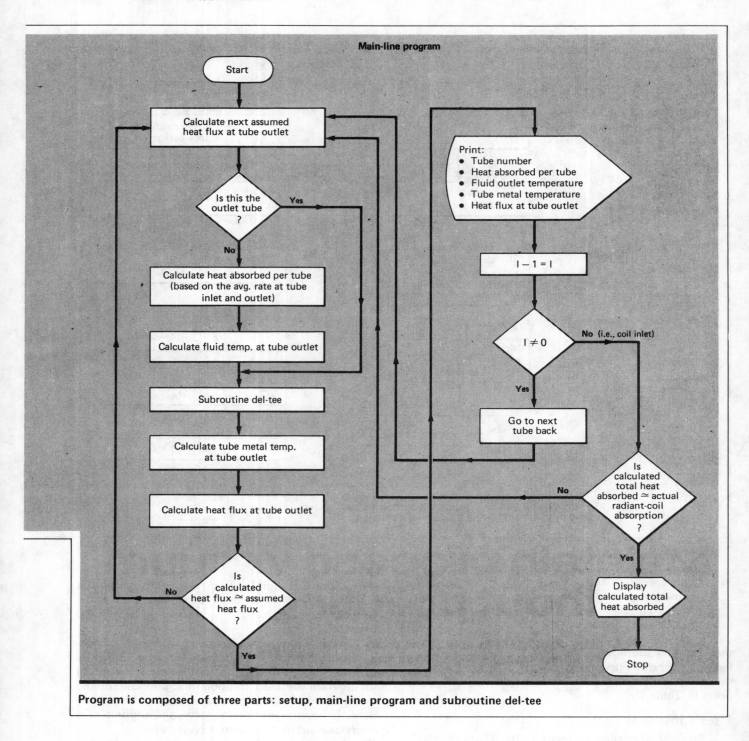

Main-line program

Start

Calculate next assumed heat flux at tube outlet

Is this the outlet tube ? — Yes

No

Calculate heat absorbed per tube (based on the avg. rate at tube inlet and outlet)

Calculate fluid temp. at tube outlet

Subroutine del-tee

Calculate tube metal temp. at tube outlet

Calculate heat flux at tube outlet

Is calculated heat flux ≃ assumed heat flux ? — No

Yes

Print:
• Tube number
• Heat absorbed per tube
• Fluid outlet temperature
• Tube metal temperature
• Heat flux at tube outlet

$I - 1 = I$

$I \neq 0$ — No (i.e., coil inlet)

Yes

Go to next tube back

Is calculated total heat absorbed ≃ actual radiant-coil absorption ? — No

Yes

Display calculated total heat absorbed

Stop

Program is composed of three parts: setup, main-line program and subroutine del-tee

(°F/ft)—is built into the program. Note T_{BW} is 1,728°F.

The heat flux was guessed to be 8,000 Btu/(h)(ft²). Results of the calculations are shown in Table III. ABS stands for heat absorbed per tube, in Btu/h. RATE is heat flux, Btu/(h)(ft²). Note that T_{MT} is symbolized by TMT, and T_{FO} is symbolized by FOT. Similar substitutions are made elsewhere.

For HP-67/97 users

Two programs are required to perform these calculations on the HP calculators. Table IV provides a listing of both programs A and B, and Table V gives the operating steps necessary to run the program. After entering the data, it is wise to record them on a separate magnetic card. Also, recording each of the programs on magnetic cards facilitates the running of the programs and preserves the programs for later use. As in the TI version, when **KEY A** is pressed, the program lists all data registers. When **KEY E** is pressed (Step 7), the tube number, heat absorbed, fluid temperature, tube-metal temperature and heat flux at the oulet of each tube are printed. Finally, the total heat absorbed in the coil is printed. If this value is not close enough to the actual value of heat absorbed, return to step 2 and continue. Data entry may be made via magnetic card. Table VI describes the user-defined keys, flags, and data storage locations for the HP version.

Program Listing for HP version

Table IV

Step	Key	Code	Step	Key	Code	Step	Key	Code	Step	Key	Code	Step	Key	Code
Program A			048	RCL2	36 02	034	÷	-24	083	SPC	16-11	132	ST09	35 09
			049	-	-45	035	ST01	35 01	084	P≠S	16-51	133	P≠S	16-51
001	*LBLA	21 11	050	RCL4	36 04	036	RCL4	36 04	085	RCL1	36 01	134	RCL9	36 09
002	FREG	16-13	051	RCL5	36 05	037	RCL1	36 01	086	PRTX	-14	135	P≠S	16-51
003	P≠S	16-51	052	-	-45	038	RCL8	36 08	087	P≠S	16-51	136	RCL8	36 08
004	PREG	16-13	053	÷	-24	039	÷	-24	088	ST+7	35-55 07	137	P≠S	16-51
005	P≠S	16-51	054	STOE	35 15	040	-	-45	089	RCLB	36 12	138	RCL9	36 09
006	R/S	51	055	RCL4	36 04	041	STOB	35 12	090	PRTX	-14	139	1	01
007	*LBLB	21 12	056	STOB	35 12	042	P≠S	16-51	091	RCLC	36 13	140	2	02
008	ST00	35 00	057	CLX	-51	043	*LBL1	21 01	092	PRTX	-14	141	÷	-24
009	ST02	35 02	058	P≠S	16-51	044	GSB2	23 02	093	RCL2	36 02	142	-	-45
010	P≠S	16-51	059	ST07	35 07	045	P≠S	16-51	094	PRTX	-14	143	3	03
011	RCL4	36 04	060	R/S	51	046	RCLB	36 12	095	SPC	16-11	144	6	06
012	P≠S	16-51				047	+	-55	096	RCLB	36 12	145	x	-35
013	ST01	35 01	**Program B**			048	STOC	35 13	097	P≠S	16-51	146	÷	-24
014	RCL3	36 03				049	RCL6	36 06	098	ST04	35 04	147	P≠S	16-51
015	RCL9	36 09	001	*LBLE	21 15	050	RCLD	36 14	099	P≠S	16-51	148	ST03	35 03
016	÷	-24	002	P≠S	16-51	051	4	04	100	DSZI	16 25 46	149	RCL6	36 06
017	ST04	35 04	003	0	00	052	6	06	101	GTOC	22 13	150	1	01
018	RCL5	36 05	004	ST01	35 01	053	0	00	102	RCL1	36 01	151	2	02
019	1	01	005	P≠S	16-51	054	+	-55	103	P≠S	16-51	152	x	-35
020	2	02	006	RCL4	36 04	055	4	04	104	ST04	35 04	153	P≠S	16-51
021	÷	-24	007	1	01	056	Y^x	31	105	P≠S	16-51	154	RCL0	36 00
022	RCL6	36 06	008	+	-55	057	RCLC	36 13	106	RCL7	36 07	155	P≠S	16-51
023	6	06	009	STOI	35 46	058	4	04	107	PRTX	-14	156	RCL5	36 05
024	÷	-24	010	STOA	35 11	059	6	06	108	SPC	16-11	157	RCL6	36 06
025	-	-45	011	*LBLC	21 13	060	0	00	109	SPC	16-11	158	-	-45
026	ST08	35 08	012	RCL2	36 02	061	+	-55	110	R/S	51	159	x	-35
027	RCL3	36 03	013	RCL0	36 00	062	4	04	111	*LBL2	21 02	160	÷	-24
028	RCL7	36 07	014	+	-55	063	Y^x	31	112	RCLE	36 15	161	RCL0	36 00
029	Pi	16-24	015	2	02	064	-	-45	113	RCLB	36 12	162	RCL5	36 05
030	RCL5	36 05	016	÷	-24	065	x	-35	114	P≠S	16-51	163	1	01
031	x	-35	017	1	01	066	P≠S	16-51	115	RCL5	36 05	164	2	02
032	x	-35	018	0	00	067	ST02	35 02	116	-	-45	165	÷	-24
033	x	-35	019	0	00	068	RCL0	36 00	117	x	-35	166	x	-35
034	1	01	020	+	-55	069	-	-45	118	RCL2	36 02	167	RCL9	36 09
035	2	02	021	ST00	35 00	070	ABS	16 31	119	+	-55	168	RCL3	36 03
036	÷	-24	022	RCLI	36 46	071	1	01	120	P≠S	16-51	169	+	-55
037	RCL4	36 04	023	RCLA	36 11	072	0	00	121	RCL8	36 08	170	X≠Y	-41
038	÷	-24	024	X≤Y?	16-35	073	0	00	122	P≠S	16-51	171	R↓	-31
039	P≠S	16-51	025	GT01	22 01	074	X≠Y	-41	123	RCL9	36 09	172	+	-55
040	ST07	35 07	026	*LBL3	21 03	075	X≤Y?	16-35	124	6	06	173	R↑	16-31
041	RCL3	36 03	027	RCL2	36 02	076	GTOa	22 16 11	125	÷	-24	174	x	-35
042	RCL4	36 04	028	RCL0	36 00	077	GTOC	22 13	126	-	-45	175	RTN	24
043	RCL5	36 05	029	+	-55	078	*LBLa	21 16 11	127	x	-35	176	R/S	51
044	-	-45	030	P≠S	16-51	079	RCLI	36 46	128	1	01			
045	÷	-24	031	RCL7	36 07	080	1	01	129	X≠Y	-41			
046	ST08	35 08	032	x	-35	081	-	-45	130	÷	-24			
047	RCL1	36 01	033	2	02	082	PRTX	-14	131	P≠S	16-51			

User instructions for HP version · Table V

Step	Procedure	Enter	Press	Display
1	Turn calculator on			
2	Load program A			
3	Enter data:			
	a) Number of radiant tubes	#	STO 3	#
	b) Outer diameter of tube, in.	O.D.	STO 5	O.D.
	c) Average tube wall thickness, in.	t_a	STO 6	t_a
	d) Effective tube length, in.	L	STO 7	L
	e) Number of passes	#	STO 9	#
			P≤S	
	f) Tube-metal conductivity, Btu/(h)(ft^2)(^{0}F/in.)	k_w	STO 0	k_w
	g) Inside film coefficient at coil outlet, Btu/(h)(ft^2)(^{0}F)	h_{io}	STO 1	h_{io}
	h) Inside film coefficient at coil inlet, Btu/(h)(ft^2)(^{0}F)	h_{ii}	STO 2	h_{ii}
	i) Total heat absorbed in radiant coil, Btu/h	Q	STO 3	Q
	j) Fluid temp. at coil outlet, °F	T_{FO}	STO 4	T_{FO}
	k) Fluid temp. at coil inlet, °F	T_{FI}	STO 4	T_{FI}
	l) Constant, Btu/(h)(ft^2)(R^4)	K	STO 6	K
	m) Thickness of coke deposit, in.	t_c	STO 9	t_c
	n) Bridgewall temp., °F	T_{BW}	STO D	T_{BW}
			P≤S	
4	List data registers if desired		A	
5	Enter heat flux guess and execute	Guess	B	
6	Load program B			
7	Execute		E	See text

Program information for HP version · Table VI

User defined keys

Program A

A - List data registers

B - Enter heat-flux guess
   and execute

Program B

E - Execute

Flags

None

Data registers

Primary					
0	q_{ASSD}		A	L	
1	Used		B	T_{FO}	
2	q_{CALC}		C	T_{MT}	
3	Used		D	T_{BW}	
4	I		E	Film coeff.	
5	O.D.			gradient	
6	t_a		I	Index	
7	Used				
8	Used				
9	Used				

Secondary		
0	k_w	
1	Used	
2	h_{ii}	
3	Used	
4	T_{FO}	
5	T_{FI}	
6	K	
7	A_T	
8	Temp. gradient	
9	t_c	

References

1. Amer. Petroleum Inst., publication RP-530, "Recommended Practice for the Calculation of Heater Tube Thickness," 2nd ed., Dec. 1976.
2. Carnahan, Brice, et al., "Applied Numerical Methods," John Wiley & Sons, Inc., New York, 1969.

The author

Tayseer A. Abdel-Halim is a process engineer with the Process Plant Div. of KTI Corp., 221 East Walnut St., Pasadena, CA 91101. Tel: (213) 577-1600, x284. He is involved with the design of ethylene plants. He has also worked for Born, Inc., where he was responsible for the design and cost estimation of direct-fired heaters, and for Heat Research Corp., as a senior process engineer. Abdel-Halim obtained a B.Sc. degree in refinery engineering from the Egyptian High Inst. for Petroleum Engineering, and an M.Sc. degree in chemical engineering from the University of Tulsa. He is a member of AIChE.

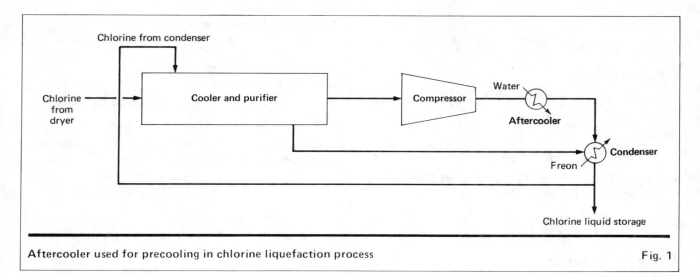

Aftercooler used for precooling in chlorine liquefaction process   Fig. 1

assumptions regarding the IC/AC applications, and assumes no ready access to their design intricacies. The assumptions are:

■ The performance of the IC/AC at design conditions is known from the manufacture's predictions or experimentation.

■ The overall heat-transfer coefficient, U, remains constant for the original exchanger design and new operating conditions.

■ The off-design conditions result from reasonable deviations in flowrates for both the hot gas and coolant (i.e., changes of not more than 25%).

■ The fluids entering the IC/AC are unmixed, traveling separate paths by tubes or channels.

Basis of the method

This method uses NTU (number of transfer units) and heat-exchanger-effectiveness relationships to predict performance at an alternate operating point by comparing the actual IC/AC performance to that of an ideal model [design] performance, and determining how the ideal model performance is affected by changing parameters. The parameters of concern generally are the gas and liquid flowrates, and entering and exiting temperature of both gas and coolant.

In instances where other parameters, such as relative humidity and operating pressure, deviate from design conditions, their effect on performance should be evaluated by other known methods. However, these parameters will not have a significant impact on the procedure discussed here.

The standard NTU and heat-exchanger relationships used by exchanger designers are as follows for the three types of exchangers [1]:

Counterflow

$$\epsilon = \frac{1 - e^{-NTU(1-R)}}{1 - Re^{-NTU(1-R)}} \qquad (1)$$

Counterflow is one of three exchanger types   Fig. 2

Nomenclature

A	Heat-transfer area, ft^2
C	Flowstream capacity rate, Btu/(h)(°F)
c	Specific heat, Btu/(lb)(°F)
NTU	Number of transfer units, dimensionless, $\left(NTU = \dfrac{UA}{C_g}\right)$
R	Capacity rate ratio, dimensionless
T	Temperature, °F
U	Overall heat-transfer coefficient, Btu/(h)(ft^2)(°F)
W	Mass flowrate, lb/h
ϵ	Heat exchanger effectiveness, dimensionless
η	$NTU^{-.22}$

Subscripts

1	Entering condition
2	Exiting condition
g	gas
l	liquid

Crossflow

$$\epsilon = 1 - e^{[[e^{(-R\eta NTU)} - 1] \, 1/\eta R]} \qquad (2)$$

Parallel-flow

$$\epsilon = \frac{1 - e^{-NTU(1+R)}}{1 + R} \qquad (3)$$

where:

$$R = C_g/C_l \qquad (4)$$

and $C_g = W_g \times c_g$, $C_l = W_l \times c_l$, $\eta = NTU^{-.22}$

The heat effectiveness is also represented by:

$$\epsilon = \frac{T_{g1} - T_{g2}}{T_{g1} - T_{l1}} \qquad (5)$$

Using the procedure

Step 1—Using the original design conditions, calculate C_g, C_l, R (Eq. 4), and ϵ (Eq. 5).

Step 2—Now using the appropriate heat-exchanger-effectiveness relationship—Eq. (1), (2) or (3)—calculate the design NTU.

Step 3—After calculating C_g and C_l for the new operating conditions, determine the NTU from the following relationship:

$$NTU_{new} = NTU_{design} \times \frac{C_{g\,design}}{C_{g\,new}} \qquad (6)$$

which is obtained from $NTU = UA/C_g$, when UA is assumed constant.

Step 4—After recalculating R for the new conditions, calculate the effectiveness, using the same equation used in Step 2.

Step 5—The new effectiveness can be used in Eq. (5), which is then solved for the exiting-gas temperature, T_{g2}.

An example

To illustrate the technique, let us calculate the change in performance (T_{g2}) for a water-cooled counterflow aftercooler used on an air compressor. The original design and new conditions are:

	Design	New
W_g	53.5 lb/min	62.06 lb/min
W_l	8.0 gal/min	6.0 gal/min
T_{g1}	250°F	275°F
T_{g2}	100°F	?
T_{l1}	60°F	80°F

and $c_g = 0.241$ Btu/(lb)(F) for air; $c_l = 0.999$ Btu/(lb)(F) for water at 60°F.

Following Step 1, the design parameters C_g and C_l are determined:

$$C_g = (53.5)(60)(0.241)$$
$$C_g = 774 \text{ Btu}/(h)(°F)$$

and

$$C_l = (8.0)(60)(62.4)(0.134)(0.999)$$
$$C_l = 4014 \text{ Btu}/(h)(°F)$$

Using Eq. (4), calculate R_{design}:

$$R_{design} = 774/4014$$
$$R_{design} = 0.193$$

and find ϵ by using Eq. (5)

$$\epsilon_{design} = 250 - 100/250 - 60$$
$$\epsilon_{design} = 0.79$$

Since the type of aftercooler design used is a counterflow type, Eq. (1) is used to determine NTU_{design}:

$$0.79 = \frac{1 - e^{-NTU(1-0.193)}}{1 - 0.193 \, e^{-NTU(1-0.193)}}$$

$$NTU_{design} = 1.722$$

For Step 3, C_g and C_l are calculated for the new operating conditions:

$$C_g = (62.06)(60)(0.241)$$
$$C_g = 897 \text{ Btu}/(h)(°F)$$

and

$$C_l = (6.0)(62.4)(60)(0.134)(0.999)$$
$$C_l = 3010 \text{ Btu}/(h)(°F)$$

NTU_{new} can now be calculated from Eq. (6):

$$NTU_{new} = 1.73 \times (774/897)$$
$$NTU_{new} = 1.49$$

The new R is found using Eq. (4) and is then used in Eq. (1) to determine the new ϵ:

$$R_{new} = 897/3010$$
$$R_{new} = 0.298$$

and

$$\epsilon_{new} = \frac{1 - e^{-1.49(1-0.298)}}{1 - 0.298e^{-1.49(1-0.298)}}$$

$$\epsilon_{new} = 0.725$$

Finally, the new ϵ is used in Eq. (5), which is solved for T_{g2}:

$$0.725 = (275 - T_{g2}/275 - 80)$$
$$T_{g2} = 134°F$$

References

1. Desmond, R. M., and Karlekar, B. V., "Engineering Heat Transfer," West Publishing Co., St. Paul, Minn., 1977.

The author

Peter Y. Burke is director of engineering at Sundstrand Fluid Handling, a unit of Sundstrand Corp., P.O. Box FH, Arvada, CO 80004; telephone: 303-425-0800. A professional engineer in New York and Maryland, he previously worked as a product manager at Worthington Engineered Pump, a division of the Worthington Pump Co. He holds a B.S. in mechanical engineering from Virginia Polytechnic Institute and an M.S. in the same subject from Rensselaer Polytechnic Institute. He is a member of the National Management Assn.

Are liquid thermal-relief valves needed?

Thermal stresses, or pressures from hydrogen evolution due to corrosion, can rupture a pipe or tube. Here is how to find such forces to see whether a relief valve is needed.

Sudhir R. Brahmbhatt, MG Industries

☐ In protecting process pipelines, engineers seldom perform calculations to see whether thermal stresses or pressure buildups (as a result of H_2 evolution from corrosion) exist. Such neglect could lead to rupture, especially if relief valves have not been employed.

Here, we present a calculation method that will determine whether or not a relief valve is required. An example illustrates the method.

Thermal expansion and corrosion

In the case of thermal expansion, when pipes, tubes or process equipment are full of liquid and are blocked in, rupture can result from heat from several sources:
- Solar radiation.
- Heat-tracing coils.
- Heat transfer by radiation and conduction from nearby process equipment.

A typical example would be a heat exchanger blocked-in on the cold side, with flow continuing on the hot side. Such a situation could occur during normal operation, e.g., when a hot product-stream was being pumped through an exchanger to a flash drum and the stream was being used to preheat the feed to a reactor. If a level controller that operated a control valve between the exchanger and flash drum were to close the control valve, the feed would be blocked in.

Then, of course, the system can be subject to thermal expansion. Stresses result from the difference in coefficients of thermal expansion between the liquid and the metal.

On the other hand, corrosion, which generates hydrogen, can also give rise to severe stresses caused by gas pressure. Such a case may occur when, for example, the flow of sulfuric acid is stopped in a steel pipeline and it remains full. After some time, enough hydrogen may be generated to create pressures that will burst the pipe.

To see whether a relief valve is needed, the stresses due to thermal expansion and corrosion must first be found. Here is a method to do this:

Determining thermal stresses

The net volume of liquid that expands is found by subtracting the pipe expansion due to both temperature rise and pressure rise from the liquid volume expansion due to temperature rise:

$$\Delta V = (V_t - V_{to}) - \Delta V_p - \Delta V_{Pr} \qquad (1)$$

The volumetric expansion of the liquid at temperature t above a reference temperature is given by:

$$V_t = V_{tr}(1 + at + bt^2 + ct^3) \qquad (2)$$

The reference temperature tr is 0°C. Values of a, b, and c are given for some liquids in Table I.

When a liquid expands from temperature to to temperature t, its volume at t is:

$$V_t = V_{to} + V_{tr}[a(t - to) + b(t^2 - to^2) + c(t^3 - to^3)] \qquad (3)$$

The pipe expansion due to temperature is given by:

$$\Delta V_p = \pi/4[(D + CD)^2(L + CL) - D^2L] \qquad (4)$$

In Eq. (4), L is the total pipe length including fittings, i.e., it must account for the total restricted fluid volume. Typical values of C appear in Table II.

The increase in pressure of the liquid—due either to heat or to gas buildup—will expand the pipe further [1]. Such an increase is usually minimal when compared with the effects of heat alone, and can be ignored in making calculations. However, an equation for this effect (pipe expansion due to pressure) is presented:

$$\Delta V_{Pr} = [\pi (\Delta R)^2] L + \pi R^2 [\Delta L]$$
$$= \pi L \left[\frac{R}{E}\left(\frac{PR}{T_h} - \gamma \frac{PR}{2T_h}\right)\right]^2 + \pi R^2 \left[P \frac{L}{E} \frac{A_{ID}}{A_{metal}}\right] \qquad (5)$$

Poisson's ratio, γ, is 0.3 for steel and Alloy 20, as given in the American Natl. Standards Institute (ANSI), New York, ANSI Standard 31.3. Liquid compressibility is defined as:

$$\beta = -\left(\frac{\text{Final volume} - \text{Initial volume}}{\text{Final pressure} - \text{Initial pressure}}\right) \times \qquad (6)$$
$$\left(\frac{1}{\text{Initial volume}}\right)$$

For a liquid of volume V_t in a pipe of fixed volume V_{to}, β is expressed as:

$$\beta = -\left(\frac{V_{to} - V_t}{\Delta P} \frac{1}{V_t}\right) \qquad (7)$$

Originally published May 14, 1984

Coefficients of cubical expansion for some typical liquids | Table I

Liquid	Range, °C	a^*, 10^{-3}	b, 10^{-6}	c, 10^{-8}
Benzene	11- 81	1.17626	1.27755	0.80646
Toluene	0-100	1.028	1.779	—
Methyl alcohol	−38+70	1.18557	1.56493	0.91113
n-Butyl alcohol	6-108	0.83751	2.8634	−0.12415
iso-Propyl alcohol	0- 83	1.04345	0.44303	2.7274
Chloroform	0- 63	1.10715	4.66473	−1.74328
Carbon tetrachloride	0- 76	1.18384	0.89881	1.35135
Ethyl acetate	−36+72	1.2585	2.95688	0.14922
Hydrochloric acid, 33.2%	0- 33	0.4460	0.215	—
Sulfuric acid, conc.	0- 60	0.5758	−0.864	—
n-Pentane	−190+30	1.50697	3.435	0.975

The coefficients are for $tr = 0°C$

*For example, for benzene: $V = V_{tr}[1 + 1.17626 \times 10^{-3} t + 1.2775 \times 10^{-6} t^2 + 0.80646 \times 10^{-8} t^3]$

From Ref. [2].

Coefficients of linear thermal expansion for a few typical alloys | Table II

Temperature, °F	Carbon steel	18-8 stainless steel	25-Cr 20-Ni	Wrought iron
50	−0.14	−0.21	−0.16	−0.16
70	0	0	0	0
100	0.23	0.34	0.28	0.26
125	0.42	0.62	0.51	0.48
200	0.99	1.46	1.21	1.14
250	1.40	2.03	1.70	1.60
300	1.82	2.61	2.18	2.06
400	2.70	3.80	3.20	3.01
500	3.62	5.01	4.24	3.99
700	5.63	7.50	6.44	6.06
900	7.81	10.12	8.78	8.26

From Ref. [5].

Compressibilities of some selected liquids | Table III

Liquid	Temperature, °C	Pressure, atm	β, 10^{-6}, atm
Ethyl alcohol	20	1-50	112
	20	200-300	86
Methyl alcohol	0	1-500	79.4
n-Butyl alcohol	17.4	8	90
iso-Butyl alcohol	17.95	8	98
n-Propyl alcohol	0	1-500	69
iso-Propyl alcohol	5.65	8	95
	17.85	8	103
Chloroform	20	0-98.7	94.9
	100	8-9	211
Ethyl acetate	13.3	8.1-37.4	104
	99.6	8.13-37.15	250
Benzene	20	1-2	95.3
	20	98.7-197.4	58.4
Toluene	10	1-5.25	79
	100	1-5.25	150
Sulfuric acid, 70%, wt.	60.3	(wide range)	50-100
Water	0	1-25	52.5
	100	100-200	46.8

From Ref. [2, 4].

Nomenclature

a, b, c	Coefficients for Eq. (2)
A	Surface area of pipe in contact with liquid, ft²
A_{ID}	Pipe cross-sectional area, ft²
A_{metal}	Cross-sectional area of pipe metal (of the "ring" of a section of pipe), ft²
C	Coefficient of linear thermal expansion of pipe material, ft/ft
C_R	Corrosion rate, mils/yr
D	Pipe inside dia., ft
E	Modulus of elasticity, lb/in²
H	Henry's law constant, atm
L	Pipe length between block valves, ft
L_m	Gas evolved, moles H_2/wk
M_p	Hydrogen equivalent weight of pipe material, moles
P	Pressure, psi or atm
ΔP	Pressure change due to thermal stresses, psi or atm
ΔP_c	Pressure change due to corrosion, psi or atm
R	Pipe radius, ft
T_h	Pipe thickness, ft
t	Temperature, °F or °C
t_{avg}	Average temperature, °F or °C
t_r	Reference temperature, here 0°C
V_t	Volume of liquid at t, ft³
V_{to}	Volume of liquid at to, ft³
V_{tr}	Volume of liquid at tr, ft³
ΔV	Net volume change, ft³
ΔV_p	Pipe volume change due to temperature rise, ft³
ΔV_{pr}	Pipe volume change due to pressure rise, ft³
$\Delta V_{thermal}$	Liquid volume expansion due to temperature rise, ft³
X_L	Amount of liquid in pipe, moles

Greek letters

β	Liquid compressibility, atm^{-1}
γ	Poisson's ratio
ρ_p	Pipe material density, lb/ft³

Eq. (7) can be rearranged and expressed in terms of the coefficients of liquid volume expansion to yield the following expression:

$$\Delta P = \left(\frac{1}{\beta}\right)\left(\frac{a(t - to) + b(t^2 - to^2) + c(t^3 - to^3)}{1 + at + bt^2 + ct^3}\right) \quad (8)$$

Usually, $(V_t - V_{to})$ is much greater than ΔV_p and ΔV_{Pr}. Thus, Eq. (7) is generally sufficient for calculating the pressure rise due to thermal stresses.

Determining stresses due to corrosion

In an aqueous medium, the corrosion reaction of a metal may be represented by:

$$\text{Metal} + H_2O \rightarrow H_2 + \text{Metal oxide} \quad (9)$$

One mole of hydrogen is released for every mole of

bivalent metal that reacts. If L_m is the moles of hydrogen evolved/wk, then:

$$L_m = \left(C_R, \frac{\text{mils}}{\text{yr}}\right) \left(\frac{\text{in.}}{1,000 \text{ mils}}\right) \left(\frac{\text{ft}}{12 \text{ in.}}\right) (A) (\rho_p) \times$$
$$\left(\frac{\text{mole}}{M_p}\right) \left(\frac{\text{yr}}{52 \text{ wk}}\right) =$$
$$\left(\frac{1}{624 \times 10^3}\right) \left(\frac{C_R A \rho_p}{M_p}\right), \text{moles/wk} \quad (10)$$

The number of moles of H_2 evolved will vary if the valence of the metal is different. Such an effect must be accounted for in calculations.

Using Henry's law (i.e., the solubility of a gas in a liquid—its mole fraction—is directly proportional to the pressure of the gas above the liquid), the pressure rise is:

$$\Delta P_c = H \left(\frac{L_M}{X_L + L_M}\right) \quad (11)$$

H, Henry's law constant, is available in the literature. Eq. (11) is based on the following assumptions: (1) H is not a function of pressure; (2) the hydrogen gas-phase is ideal; (3) the pipe is full of liquid and the liquid is incompressible; and (4) the pipe is rigid.

Eq. (11) gives an approximate pressure rise for one week with no flow in the pipe.

Example

A 4-in. Alloy 20, Sch. 10 pipeline is used to transport 70% H_2SO_4. The pipe's pressure rating is 500 psi and its I.D. is 4.26 in. The temperature is expected to rise occasionally to 130°F (54.8°C) from its normal value of 100°F (38.1°C). The pipeline could be out of service for up to one week. The distance between block valves is 9,900 ft. Is a thermal-relief valve needed?

Consider the worst case—130°F and 1 wk. From Table I, for 70% H_2SO_4, use the volume for concentrated sulfuric acid, which is expressed as:

$$V_t = V_{to} + V_{tr}[0.5758 \times 10^{-3}$$
$$(t - to) - 0.864 \times 10^{-6}(t^2 - to^2)] \quad (12)$$

Eq. (12) is written in °C. The coefficient of linear thermal expansion for Alloy 20 (25Cr, 20Ni) is, from Table II, 0.556 in./100 ft, or 46.3×10^{-3} ft/100 ft.

Calculate the liquid volume expansion due to the temperature rise. In Eq. (12), substituting the following:

$$t - to = 16.7 \text{ °C, and } to = 38.1°C$$

and rearranging, yields:

$$\left(\frac{V_t - V_{to}}{V_{to}}\right) =$$
$$\left(\frac{0.5758 \times 10^{-3} (16.7) - 0.864 \times 10^{-6} (54.8^2 - 38.1^2)}{1 + 0.5758 \times 10^{-3} (38.1) - 0.864 \times 10^{-6} (38.1)^2}\right) =$$
$$\frac{0.008275}{1.020684} = 0.008107 \quad (13)$$

The initial volume of acid in the pipe is:

$$V_{to} = (\pi/4)D^2L =$$
$$(\pi/4)(4.26/12)^2(9,900) = 979.9 \text{ ft}^3 \quad (14)$$

And the change in volume is:

$$\Delta V_t = 979.9 \times 0.008107 = 7.94 \text{ ft}^2 \quad (15)$$

Calculate the pressure rise due to the liquid volume expansion. Rewriting Eq. (7) and substituting values from Eq. (13) into it:

$$\Delta P = - \left(\frac{V_{to} - V_t}{\beta}\right) \left(\frac{1}{V_t}\right) =$$
$$- \left(\frac{V_{to} - (V_{to} + 0.008107 \, V_{to})}{V_{to}(1.008107)}\right) \left(\frac{1}{\beta}\right) =$$
$$\left(\frac{0.008042}{\beta}\right) \quad (16)$$

From Table III, β for 70% H_2SO_4 is: $50 \times 10^{-6} < \beta < 100 \times 10^{-6}$. Thus, substituting into Eq. (16) yields: 80 atm $< \Delta P <$ 160 atm. Calculations for ΔV_{Pr} and ΔV_p are omitted, since they are assumed to be much smaller than the above-calculated pressure rise. Now, the pressure rise due to corrosion is calculated.

The corrosion rate for Alloy 20 in H_2SO_4 at 54.8°C is about 5 mils/yr. Assume that this value is accurate enough. The density of Alloy 20 is 499 lb/ft³, and M_p is 50.8. M_p is calculated by multiplying the moles $\times$ valence/2 for each element in an alloy and adding up the total of such terms. Substituting into Eq. (10):

$$L_m = \left(\frac{1}{624 \times 10^3}\right) \left(\frac{5\pi (4.26/12) \, 9,900 \times 499}{50.8}\right) =$$
$$0.87 \text{ moles of } H_2 \text{ generated/wk} \quad (17)$$

The moles of H_2SO_4 in the pipe are:

979.9 ft³ $\times$ 115.19 lb/ft³ $\times$ (1/98) mole/lb = 1,152 moles; where 115.19 lb/ft³ is the density of sulfuric acid and 98 is its molecular weight.

Henry's law constant for H_2 in water at 20°C is 6.83×10^4 atm. Thus:
$\Delta P_c = (6.83 \times 10^4)[0.87/(1,152 + 0.87)] = 51.5$ atm, or about 760 psi in one week.

A relief valve is needed, since the pressure calculated due to either heat or corrosion (or certainly from both) exceeds the design pressure of the piping.

References

1. Roark, R. J., "Formulas for Stress and Strain," 3rd ed., 1954, McGraw-Hill Book Co., New York, p. 268.
2. Lange, N. A., ed., "Handbook of Chemistry," 10th ed., 1961, McGraw-Hill Book Co., New York, pp. 1670-1679.
3. Mukerji, A., How to Size Relief Valves, Chem. Eng., June 2, 1980, Vol. 87, No. 11, p. 79.
4. Hodgman, P. C., ed., "Handbook of Chemistry and Physics," 32nd ed., 1950, Chemical Rubber Publishing Co., Cleveland, pp. 1803-1805.
5. Weaver, R., "Process Piping Design," Vol. II, Gulf Pub. Co., Houston, 1973, p. 155.

The author

Sudhir R. Brahmbhatt is an applications engineer for the Gas Products div. of MG Industries, P.O. Box 945, Valley Forge, PA 19482. Tel: (215) 630-5400. His work includes developing process alternatives, selecting processes, and designing energy-saving systems. Previously, he was a senior process engineer with Air Products & Chemicals, Inc. He holds a bachelor's degree in chemical engineering from Nadiad Inst. of Technology (India), an M.S. in chemical engineering from Stevens Inst. of Technology, and an M.B.A. from Fairleigh Dickinson University. He is a member of AIChE.